Dedication

In Fond Memory of My Parents

Untouchables among Dalits

From the Lowest of the Low

J. Bheemaiah

Prestige Books International
New Delhi

Published by
Prestige Books International
New Delhi 110 060
prestigebooks@gmail.com
Phone: 9818755529, 9810323134

ISBN: 978-81-956029-4-0

Printed in India

Contents

Foreword

The Constitution of India vis-à-vis Articles 15 and 17 is crystal clear about its stance against caste discriminations which degrade human personality of certain sections of people who are branded as Dalits as it is the case in India. Despite Constitutional assurances on paper, Caste system still prevails and is deeply entrenched in various forms not only in India but across Asia, and even among the Indian diaspora in the West. It is travesty of fairness and justice that, even in this era of global enlightenment that seeks empowerment that ensures dignity for all without discrimination, civil societies and communities are stuck up with tradition-bound attitudes which impose 'taint of pollution' upon dalits in the name of untouchability. It is all the more hurting and painful to know that it is often the lowest of the low among the so-called 'untouchables' who are constrained to endure more acutely the inhuman phenomenon of discrimination in the name of caste exploitation and subcultures of caste oppression. It is against this backdrop that this trim book is of great relevance and importance. The apt title of the book reveals the aim, purpose, and design of the research project taken up by the author.

In plain language, with clarity of purpose, lucidity of thought and expression and ample down-to-earth stories and examples, the author delineates how the least among the untouchables of India—Baindlas, Chindus, and Dakkalis—are destined to view themselves and are viewed by hierarchic and hegemonic caste-conscious communities around them. The angst articulated in the book is about stigmatization in terms of marginalization, endured all the more from within the left vs the right tension among dalits themselves. With a number of instances gathered from field studies the author succinctly focuses on how marginalization, 'triple marginalization of dalit women' all the more, operates in multiple layers in vicious cyclic circles in Indian society paving the way for 'superstructures' and sub-cultures of marginalization. In between the lines, the author narrates heart-warming stories, like that of Mogulaiah, the award-winning musician, who despite amazing talent and admiration from music lovers, continues to live in abject poverty in the midst of economic misery and sub-caste marginalization. Reading these stories should prick our social conscience with compunctious 'vistings of Nature', to use a phrase of Shakespeare.

The author's empathetic witnessing and commitment to authentic narration lies in his true-to-life perception of the existential realities as observed by him. This perception serves as the matrix for his interpretation of untouchability from the point of the view of the least of the least among dalits. His averment is crystal clear, namely the life of these untouchables is a perennial endurance of experiences of being 'outed' by one or other form of social discrimination, marginalization and exclusion within and by other dalit communities who have somewhat better status within dalit-caste hierarchies. This is the rationale behind the title of the book, *Untouchables among Dalits*.

Readers familiar with the socio-politico-cultural realities of India may be aware of the antiquity of the myths of origin vis-à-vis the brahminical concept of caste system that has no qualms about perpetuating the plight of untouchables in India till date. This book is not about that antiquity although it touches upon how India's caste system serves as an agency of one's social standings of identity in India even today. Instead, it focuses on, as noted above, the painful phenomenon linked to this obnoxious antiquity, namely the social and self-exclusion of 'the least of the least among untouchables', the social exclusion being perpetuated by vicious hegemonic forces in the name of religion and caste, covertly and openly supported by conceited caste-groups and right-wing politics, and the self-exclusion endured as a sort of sub-culture under the tyranny of caste hierarchies. It is perceptively implied that both forms of exclusion are preposterous and inhuman as they negate dignity, equality, fraternity and basic human fellowship.

The methodology adopted by the author is scientific and systematic, distilled with a poetic and therapeutic touch. He connotes in-between the lines of his narration that, as Devanoora Mahadeva, author of the well-known Kannada novel, *Kusuma Baale*, states, 'human relations are far greater' than these hawkish brahminical conceptual ways of marginalizing human beings. One need not necessarily hail from a socially marginalized background to subscribe to this great truth and value and appreciate the stance taken by such writers.

A socially sensitized reading of the book will propel readers to empathize with marginalized victims, especially the least of the least within caste hierarchies, and join them in their struggle towards getting 'educated, agitated, mobilized', as Dr. B.R. Ambedkar, the author of the monograph titled, *Annihilation of Caste*, averred already in the 1930s for effecting necessary changes which could usher in a casteless humane society. That idea of India remains still as a dream. In this context, readers may be reminded of the poetic stances connoted by Mulk Raj Anand in his classic novel, *Untouchable*. A state of servitude and subjugation, tamed by caste-based concepts and prolonged by vested interests, that too in a democratic country like India, is a modern-day curse that is bound to consume and diminish the dignity of India in her pursuit towards progress and international stature. Mulk Raj Anand and Ambedkar were of the view that 'as long as India does not achieve social liberty that guarantees equal rights to all, freedom provided by law is of no avail'. This cry for freedom is a perennial struggle for 'reclamation of human personality.' In 1942, Ambedkar averred again: "With justice on our side, I do not see how we can lose our battle. The battle to me is a matter of joy. . . . For ours is a battle not for wealth or for power. It is a battle for freedom. It is a battle for the reclamation of the human personality" (*The All-India Depressed Classes Conference)*.

It is high time that we, the people of India, particularly socially conscious and concerned citizens, ask for the incorporation of "social endosmosis" into the vision and scheme of New Education Policy of India (NEP). It is a great value-concept introduced by Prof. Dewey, mentor of Ambedkar, and advocated by Ambedkar himself. It serves as the springboard for 'the natural flow and exchange of ideas, values, practices, knowledge and energies between and across groups'. *It is another name for democracy, fraternity and human fellowship.*

In this context, another article I recently read, titled "Situating Democracy in Ambedkar's Moral Discourse", by S. Telang & M. Kudupale, published in *Contemporary Voice of Dalit*, 13 December 2022, comes to my mind. It facilitates one to appreciate how and why Ambedkar 'rejected oppressive and traditional systems of caste' and why he was particular to envisage 'a moral foundation', tenable and acceptable to all, so as to 'reconstruct the concept of democracy through Buddhist principles' and through the incorporation of 'social endosmosis'.

'Social Endosmosis' stands for affirmative action that includes a fine pathway for meeting of creative minds, exchange of ideas, and nurturing human fellowship and solidarity beyond caste or religion or ghetto-community-affiliated constrictions. Against the perils of caste-constrictions which continue to perpetuate social exclusions and marginalizations which smudge the idea of India, Ambedkar's vision of a casteless society is a way forward to ensure that constitutional morality prevails in terms of equality, fraternity, and fellowship. This is why India's New Education Policy should promote social endosmosis as a foremost value through all its learning systems focusing on the dignity of every human being without discrimination. That will be a sure and natural gateway towards promoting truly a casteless society, a new India.

I congratulate Prof. J. Bheemaiah for his gentle provocations in the book which inspired me to write this foreword. I also congratulate the publishers for their support in bringing out this concise and educative book.

A.S. Dasan, Ph.D.
Formerly Professor of English and
Founder-Director of the Centre for Proficiency Development
University of Mysore

Acknowledgements

At the outset, I express my gratitude to the Indian Council of Social Sciences (ICSSR), New Delhi, for providing financial support for my research on the most backward dalit communities—Chindus, Baindlas and Dakkalis—in Telangana State during 2017-2019. It was really a great opportunity for me to visit the habitations of the dependent sub-castes in the interior villages of various districts in the State. I am indebted to Mrs. Revathi Viswanath, Assistant Director, RPS In charge (ICSSR), for extending her support and cooperation in the execution of the project.

Mr. Subbaraju Maram who worked as Research Assistant helped me to the best of his ability and knowledge in the data collection during the field visit while Ms. Eswari Bai served as a data entry operator. I thank both of them for their sincerity and commitment. I also thank Mrs. Rajani and Mr. Srisailam for their outreach and support services from the office of the Centre for Comparative Literature (CCL). I thank my colleagues at CCL and the office staff of the Dean, School of Humanities, for their cooperation.

I am grateful to Professor A.S. Dasan for his moral support and encouragement in my academic endeavours. I also thank Dr. R.K. Dhawan, University of Delhi, for his insightful suggestions and Dr. Suman Bala for her editorial advice from time to time. Finally, I thank Ms. Richa for her cooperation in the publication of this book, and also sincerely acknowledge my gratitude to Prestige Books International, New Delhi, for bringing out this book with an aesthetically designed jacket.

Hyderabad **J. Bheemaiah**

Introduction
Marginalizing the Marginalized

In the context of Indian society, caste, gender discrimination and economic disparities are setbacks for national integration and development. Besides this fact, several other factors such as religious, regional, social, racial and linguistic intrigues contribute to the process of social marginalization. The indigenous people of our country, being coerced into spatial peripheries, have been blatantly discriminated against, stigmatized, ignored and often suppressed on the basis of race, age, culture, religion, ethnicity, and occupation. The so-called mainstream society with its numerically dominant minority felt its strong presence in every human sphere. We need to understand the processes by which hegemonic societies and dominant cultural groups have marginalized a section of people for centuries in one form or the other. This is a reality in Indian society.

The marginalized social groups which have been subjugated by the dominant few are now asserting their social identity and equal rights through their vernacular writing. There is a recurring demand for social equality, freedom and liberty which have been embedded in the dalit struggles on the one hand and poised to strengthen counter-writing with a different aesthetics on the other hand.

Rural spaces are becoming part of the globalized world. Despite the changing scenario, Hindu society is still riddled with caste and religious prejudice in its social relations. Given this fact, caste is a major theme in dalit writing. Ex-untouchables were addressed with Sanskrit nomenclatures such as *Aspurushyas, Panchamas Antyajas* etc. But they were never made part of

Sanskrit learning. S.M. Mate, a Maharashtra Brahmin social reformer, called them 'asprustha.' Gandhiji christened them Harijans, the children of God. Perhaps, he might have felt that the Sanskrit term *aspurusya* was contemptuous nomenclature for Harijans. Dalit intellectuals like Dr. B.R. Ambedkar have opposed Gandhi's fond phrase. Dr. B.R. Ambedkar was of the view that coinage of special names for the so-called untouchables amounted to perpetuation of contemptuous nomenclature in its different form. In his strong reaction, P.L. Mimroth, the convener of the Centre for Dalit Human Rights (CDHR), pointed out: "You will appreciate that literal word of 'Harijan' is synonymous to illegitimate child of Devadasis in olden days" (*The Hindu* 1). The Ambedkarites rejected this derogatory term conferred on the ex-untouchables of India. The term was used even in literary writings by various Indian intellectuals.

Marginality is a blanket term which cannot be confined to a particular human category. It can be perceived in many forms. Questions can be posed as to what is 'marginality' and who are 'margins? Keeping in mind the humiliating social experiences endured by reason of caste-system in India, dalits can be located in the category of 'margins' or the excluded category from the mainstream society. Many other social groups like Bahujans are in the offing to claim their identity in a different way. It is a social category with wide population. It includes dalits and minorities too. Each social category has its caste identity. Apart from this, there are several margins within the community or group. Marginality arises by reason of caste, gender, territory, language etc. For instance, women as one of the oppressed groups can also contend that they have been under patriarchal oppression for centuries and thus marginalized in many ways in the male dominated Indian society. They have been suffering repressive patriarchy and gender discrimination besides caste and sexual exploitation.

Dalit women who have been bearing the yoke of triple

oppression for centuries need to be understood as a category of the margins within the margins. Homosexuals and gays too avidly claim that they have been marginalized by other social groups. Physically disabled persons too contest their marginality in society. Can't they be differently abled-persons? Their contention runs on this line. It will be a reasonable demand for equality. Blacks in America are more marginalized by the Whites in America than African Blacks. Similarly, Dalit women are more marginalized than their upper caste counterparts. Diasporic writers also contend that they experience marginality in alien land despite the fact that they still carry with them the heritage of upper caste which subordinates lower castes in their own land where even the natives feel exotic.

In the patriarchal society, dalit woman is a margin to her husband and in return both of them become margins to an upper caste couple. An upper caste woman is a margin to her male society while she has caste superiority over a fellow woman of a lower caste. Though two women from different castes having the same patriarchal experience and economic oppression are brought together, they are projected as margins to economically dominant women groups. To me, marginality arises on factors like gender, caste, economic and physical disabilities. Inequalitics suffered by a woman are not ordained by God nor are they formulated due to biological differences. These are social and cultural constructs since all branches of knowledge are controlled and nurtured by man (Bheemaiah xvi). The concept of marginality is heterogeneous in its formulation and nature. With an immeasurable length, it is as vast as the sea in its connotation.

The element of marginality is operative in multiple layers piled up in society. Dalits are not only victims of economic oppression and exploitation but are also constrained to endure caste discriminations which contribute to the organizing process of marginalization. Caste discriminations have been meted out to dalits for centuries. It is a fact that every average Indian knows it

period, social subordination was blatantly ascribed to Sudras and *varnashramadharma* was upheld at the cost of the lower order. The relics of social inequality and discrimination practiced in the past are strongly reflected in modern society too but in different forms. Social discrimination incarnates itself into a subtle form with the same cause and effect.

'Marginality' and 'Otherness,' the social concepts, go hand in hand in their cause and effect. These terms did not merely constitute a meaning of self-alienation but they connote imposed subordination and subjugation in the specific context of caste discrimination. The privileged few perpetrated and perpetuated them against the margins. In the specific context of Indian society where caste has raised its ugly head, the margins are constituted in different domains such as caste, class, religion, gender, sexuality. Markers of marginalization tend to disguise themselves in different forms. The centre is posited against the margins. In history, ex-untouchables known as dalits today have been thrown on the periphery of the main stream society despite the fact that they were the natives of this country. The process of marginalizing the indigenous people was cleverly conspired by Aryan forces. This ended up in the four-fold system of caste which, in turn, bifurcated itself into several castes and sub-castes. Brahminism fuelled this process to the best of its pernicious nature.

The 'Other' with the capital letter 'O' is the term used very often in the postmodern period to mean the people with less significant social character in their interaction with the mainstream society which treats them as peripheral group(s) with historical invisibility. The 'Other' would also mean the people who are not just subordinated but also segregated from the mainstream social life by inhuman treatment of varna system and its consequent caste discrimination and untouchability. The Chaturvarna ladder being the fountainhead of social inequalities further created not only division of labour but also division of labourers as Dr. B.R. Ambedkar opined. Exclusion of a community is the result of not only cultural and economic disparities but also many other unequal factors in society where caste/social/racial discrimination is openly practised.

The indigenous people of India being pushed onto the peripheries are openly discriminated against, stigmatized, ignored and often suppressed on the basis of race, gender, age, culture, religion, ethnicity, occupation etc. The so-called mainstream society with its numerical minority is dominant in every aspect of human sphere. We need to understand the processes by which societies and groups have othered a section of people for centuries. The 'Other' whom the privileged castes have subordinated and subjugated are now asserting for their separate social identity, liberty and equal space in Indian society.

It is an undeniable fact that the vulnerable groups have not been adequately theorized in the mainstream literary history. Writers of the hegemonic castes have not provided a space for oppressed groups. Only faint reflections of socio-cultural history of marginalized sections are discernible in the literary stream. Some social groups are marginalized on caste and gender lines while some others have not only been marginalized but also Othered and humiliated in many ways in their relation with the mainstream Indian society.

In fact, marginality exists within marginality and 'Otherness' within Otherness, of course, in different layers and forms. Caste and sub-caste layers of existing societal pattern tend to create contradictions and conflicts. The more one goes into the depth of social layers the more one sees the marginality in its gradational and gyrational forms. So, we can't decide its static point at only one level, or in one form, or in one place. Disunity among marginalized communities for various reasons is effectively serving the social and economic purpose of the hegemonic classes within and outside their community. A small advanced section known as an elitist group which can be termed neo-bourgeois in Marxist parlance tends to go in pursuit of fulfilling its dreams at the cost of its own community rendering several others marginalized, helpless and they deny equal opportunities. It would mean that the eligible target groups are still pushed to the periphery. These elitist groups push the weak aside or keep them in slavish conditions. This group which emerges from the margins *per se* resembles a dominant minority which tends to survive at the cost of welfare of the marginalized majority. This phenomenon needs to be understood from socio-economic and political perspectives. Social disparities, unjust distribution of constitutional benefits have resulted in marginality. As such, they are destined to survive as margins deprived of adequate visibility in society. Even their political representation is not adequate. Elected representatives of these groups are not active in the welfare of their communities. Deep-rooted caste system often deters dynamism of class struggle. It is because caste lives in class and vice versa. The elite among lower sections are waging their battle for 'self-respect' because some of them have already surmounted economic problems through employment opportunities and now yearn for self-respect, social equality and dignity of life. Such self-respect movements to some extent can create space for equality but cannot liberate majority of the deprived sections from economic oppression. Self-respect movements have a tendency to benefit a group of elitist individuals among the margins. They lead the movements under their leadership. To such a category, economic problems appear very insignificant as self-respect becomes a paramount issue.

Social and economic oppression necessitate all the deprived sections of society to wage a collective struggle irrespective of castes. But caste gradation which has its dominant presence in Indian society is disintegrating the oppressed. The elitist groups refuse to join the subaltern community for class struggle. Thus, revolutionary struggles are neutralized because of class and caste divides. Exploitation of the labour class by the capitalist class is possible in any society. It can also be seen among the so-called margins. It is needless to say that Indian society comprises exploiters and the exploited; a dichotomic phenomenon is prevalent in the context of both class and caste. Exploitation is a reality in any human society across the globe, which necessitates us to remember Karl Marx today.

Marginality of a person or community is operative and it is perceived in different forms in civil societies. The force of marginality is felt and understood primarily through human interaction. At times, it is discernible even on the surface. Economic status, language, gender, region, caste, creed and colour of a person or a community can determine his/her/its status. Woman oppression continues in varied forms in all societies. Woman's participation is marginalized and devalued primarily on gender lines. Male chauvinism plays a dynamic role in regulating the woman's participation on par with men. Among the educated upper caste societies including middle and lower middle classes, it raises its ugly head. It is a very common phenomenon that a quarrel between wife and husband takes place in several households but it is often (mis)understood and projected as a power relation between the couple, which amounts to the question of patriarchy. The quarrel between wife and husband among the productive castes, as Kancha Ilaiah says, does not last long as the spouses tend to forget it and involve in daily routine. Their tussle is short-lived. In upper caste societies it is different as it amounts a patriarchal domination.

II

A female child is a margin to a male child in the same household. Very often, parents marginalize the participation of a girl-child while in pursuit of education. It happens that way for many a reason. This has been often considered gender oppression. There is another side of the coin that parents are basically ambitious about their children's education irrespective of gender. Owing to financial constraints, parents might not be able to provide education to all their children equally. Sometimes girl-children may not be given education at all. Without proper study of their economic condition, we cannot conclude it as an intentional discrimination meted out to female children within the family. Economically well-established families among the margins are providing good education to their male and female children equally.

In the downtrodden families both male and female children are equally deprived of education and they are destined to be child labourers. Parents *per se* cannot be blamed for employing their children to supplement their meagre income.

Reservation system as a constitutional measure is yet to jack up the life of the majority among the oppressed castes from the miserable condition of economic deprivation. Despite more than sixty years of its implementation, it failed to better the life of the marginalized majority. Though it placed the numerical minority in high position on the one hand, it made deprived majority individuals wait with their hands crossed at thresholds of the people of their own community on the other. It is true that the reservation system has created an upper class or creamy layer among dalits. It is because of an undemocratic enjoyment of reservation benefits by the urban few. This phenomenon has generated brahmanical attitude among the lower castes. Though this system is creating disparities among deprived sections, at least a few Dalits have become able to walk with their heads erect.

Economic disparities are growing among lower castes due to unjust implementation of reservation system. The state is yet to evolve a fair mechanism for the strict implementation of creamy layer in order to redistribute reservation benefits to the target people within the community. But it is being defeated by the 'influential class/creamy layer group' within the community. Most of the upper caste people are opposed to reservations for dalits. They should also be opposed to the illegally acquired properties of the upper castes being disproportionate to their actual income.

A person may be in the margins in terms of caste but economically one might be better than majority of his community. One may be an upper caste person but may have the experience marginality of economic conditions. As long as caste is made a strong criterion for reservation regardless of the actual economic conditions of a person or a community, this constitutional arrangement will continue to create socio-economic imbalances by the exploiting groups. Raising facts of this kind will surely invite ire from the echelons of reservation-groups. Though all people may not experience marginality equally, rural dalits have been exceptionally marginalized in almost all spheres because of caste system. The degree of marginality cannot be accurately gauged at all levels equally. Unfortunately, economically deprived and financially sound people within a community are clubbed together to constitute a sense of marginality or deprivation within the caste frame where caste stands as a parameter for economic benefit.

An individual issue may differ from that of a community. The issue of an individual is viewed from the view point of his/her community or religion but not without communal prejudice. A politician of a lower caste can never think about the welfare of his community people but whenever he gets into trouble politically, he raises hue and cry and tries to mobilize and organize his caste people to fight against the dominant upper caste forces with vested interest in the guise of his community cause. Several politicians in all communities use community card for their political survival. A solution for a few individuals cannot be the way out for the majority. We should understand the reservation system from this perspective. In fact, reservation bettered the life of a dismal number of target people while the upper castes indulged in the exploitation of caste system to enrich their vote-bank. In other words, political power moves around caste. Upper caste rulers often tend to lure reservation categories by way of extending reservations for another ten years or so. It is another way of checking the entry of the downtrodden class into political power. They thwart the efforts of the marginalized sections to win political power. It is assumed that reservations are the only way out for the emancipation of the majority oppressed. Thus, dominant upper castes conspire to perpetuate poverty and illiteracy that the marginalized people carried with them as their legacy which is a reality even today.

III

Buddha opposed caste system tooth and nail. He preached against violence and social oppression. Charvaka also rejected ritualism, Brahmnism and the authority of sacred scriptures. "The bhakti movement was a questioning of the orthodox and repressive Brahminical understanding of Hinduism and as such made it possible for the lower castes and women to give a form to their religious aspirations, emphasizing devotion and love, not knowledge, as a means of salvation" (Punekar 124).

Chokhamela, a Mahar saint of the 14th century in Maharashtra, voiced against caste system through *bhajans* and songs. He spread the message of love and equality. Undoubtedly, it was the Mahar protest voice which emerged with Chokhamela. "He is first, perhaps one of the first, if not the very first, marginalized voices in Indian history" (Punekar 125). Guru Ravidass, the 15th century chamar saint and religious reformer in the north, rejected the tradition of Brahmin mediator to reach the Supreme Being. He was of the view that one need not hide one's caste or leave one's low profession to reach God. He became a model for his fellow beings to overcome the hierarchical barriers of Brahminical social order. The religious reformers who constituted all sorts of people were associated with the Bhakti movement which has been acclaimed as a historic event because of its plurality. They strongly protested against the social marginality and preached religious equality and dignity of life.

Becoming conscious would mean getting rid of ignorance of all kinds. Consciousness evolves from one's thoughts and experiences which is a result of societal interactions. In the words of Sharankumar Limabale, 'Dalit consciousness' is an important seed for dalit literature; it is separate and distinct from the consciousness of other writers. Dalit literature is demarcated as unique because of this consciousness (32). How can a non-dalit express the pain of a victim? In that way how can non-dalits write about humiliating experiences of dalits? Dalit literature is the literature produced by dalit consciousness and from dalit point of view and with a dalit vision (Abedi 267). Abedi further elaborates: "A person with dalit viewpoint aims at limited transformation whereas a person with a dalit vision demands a total revolution or transformation. Dalit literature cannot be created out of imaginative power or close observation but by the lived experiences. Dalit writers do not seek romantic beauty in their portrayals. They are vehemently opposed to canonical literary practice. They write about harsh realities of life. They use local dialect in their writing. Their writing is neither fantastic nor imaginative but a record of oppressive life-experiences. Similes, metaphors and symbols are not important. The reality of their life is too hideously shocking, beyond the capacity of fantasy or imagination" (6).

Affirmative Indian writing came to be known as the one which is sympathetically produced by the non-dalits about dalits. "Non-dalit writing about dalit misery is admirable but one can see a deep chasm between dalit and non-dalit writing. Even if dalit and non-dalit writers have acknowledged the different nature of dalit literature and justified it, there is a minute but very sharp distinction between their two ways of thinking" (Dangle xiii).

Mulk Raj Anand, a non-dalit writer, delineates the pitiable condition of a scavenger family in the Punjab social environs. *Untouchable,* a slim but powerful novel, unravels the prejudice and repressive treatment of the orthodox Brahmin pundits, which mirrors the 1930s Indian social milieu. In fact, the novel was shaped under the guidance of Mahatma Gandhi. It has strong reflections of the Marxist perspective too. But Anand's novel is criticized as a 'discourse of pity.' The protagonist in the novel is portrayed as an object of pity, whose physical powers are neutralized and advancements are checked. The protagonist is supposed to react against sexual molestation of his sister Sohini by Pundit Kalinath. But he retreats from action. The prevalent social circumstances must have pulled back the author from propelling his hero into the social conflict. In that Anand was left with no other option but to suppress the natural emotions of his protagonist. Anand's literary sensibility created the protagonist from the lower order.

Dalit writers seem to have criticized Anand for the way he deployed and treated the protagonist. Critics need to understand that Anand endeavoured to bring to light the humiliating conditions of Bhangis representing the lower order of that time. Given the caste theme, Silia an untouchable girl in Premchand's *Godan* and Sohini in Anand's *Untouchable* are victims of seduction by the Brahmin priests. The predicament of both the girls is similar.

However, for many reasons, they cannot be considered the dalit novels, notwithstanding the portrayal of untouchable life. During the first half of twentieth century, non-dalit writers used caste as a major theme in their novels. The Telugu novel *Malapally* (1922) by Unnava Laxminarayana focuses on feudal landlord in rural India and silent suffering of the protagonist who finally dies in the jail. Premchand's *Karmabhumi* (1932) was one of the major writings which presents the problems of untouchables with a sense of realism. He was also engaged with the problem of caste throughout his literary career. Das comments: "Premchand realizes that compassion and sympathy are not enough, and individual protests are too feeble to demolish the fortress of tradition. Organized protests with a clear political and social agenda are the only weapons to fight against the caste system and rural poverty." (173)

Non-dalit writers, while exposing the problem of caste in the Indian villages, sympathetically portray the plight of untouchables. In their novels, protagonists are shown in poor light reflecting their hapless condition. Their emotions are checked and reactions neutralized. We cannot find fault with the writer for such treatment but they tried their best to represent the existing social system through characters.

In postcolonial India, first Marathi dalit literary conference was organized in 1958. Dalit writers like Baburao Bagul, Daya Pawar, Arjun Dangle, Namdeo Dhasal, Raja Dale, J.V Pawar who derived inspiration from Jotiba Phule and Dr. B.R. Ambedkar felt the need to cultivate dalit activism and writing. They began to write about the plight of dalits under the influence of Marxist ideology and emulated Black Panthers of the United States. Dalit literature proliferated with periodicals like *Ashmitadarsha* and *Amhi* edited by Gangadhar Pantavane and Baburao Bagul respectively and brought the dalit issues to limelight.

Namdeo Dhasal's *Golpita* (1973) brought a revolution in the literary world of the marginalized in general and dalits in particular. The poem delineates a number of poignant memories and critical experiences in his life in the original language of Mahars. Most of the dalit autobiographical writers used their local dialect to counter the canonical language of the mainstream writing. With his previous experience as a leader in the Labour Movement, Baburao Bagul influenced the young dalit writers who realized that there was no point to write provocative poetry against injustice. This thought led Namdeo Dhasal, Arjun Dangle and J.V. Pawar to launch the Dalit Panthers Movement in 1972 on the model of the Black Panthers Movement which could not last long due to ideological contradictions. However, the movement inspired dalit writers to promote dalit writing,

Several collections of dalit short stories were published

between 1972 and 1978. It is significant to remember that dalit literature did not first appear in the form of life narratives but mainly in the short poetic writings, life testimonies and short stories. Marathi dalit short stories like *The Poisoned Bread, The Refugee, Explosion* and the *Storeyed Building* portray the condition of the dalits in rural society. Dalits wish to lead a respectable life but their attempts are thwarted by dominant upper caste-conscious elites. Autobiography emerged as an extension of the widespread practice of short stories (Abedi 196). Writing about the self as a literary genre appears in the West in the eighteenth century; in India, dalit autobiographical writing came as a powerful literary practice much later. Marathi dalit autobiographical writing began in the nineteen sixties. For dalit writers, it became a powerful tool to assert their rights and record their protest. Constructing identity of one's own, the writers represent the entire community in dalit narratives. Dalit autobiographical narratives do not isolate the individual from his whole historical environment, family, community and society at large (Abedi 200). Dalit autobiographies have been written in all major Indian languages and they are published in English too. Autobiography is used as a vehicle by the oppressed to project their history and cultural identity. Dr. B.R. Ambedkar's *Waiting for a Visa* compiled six incidents that took place between the years 1901-38 and is a treasure of his reminiscences serving as a powerful autobiography.

The period between the years 1978-1986 is considered the autobiographical period in Marathi dalit literature. Autobiographies like Daya Pawar's *Baluta* (1978), Sonkamble's *Athavaninche Pakshi* (1982), Laxman Mane's *Upaara* (1980), Sharankumar Limbale's *Akkarmashi* (2007) and Kumud Pawade's *Antasphot* (1981) can be located in that period. *Baluta* and *Athavaninche Pakshi* speak about the endless efforts of writers to survive in the hostile, inhuman social circumstances. These autobiographies throw light on the importance of education.

K.A. Gunasekaran's *Vadu* (The Scar), a Tamil autobiography, depicts that Indian villages are doubly caste conscious, and that emancipation rests in better education.

Omprakash Valmiki's *Joothan* (1997), is a powerful personal narrative that portrays humiliating experiences of the author at the hands of upper caste Tyagi teachers in a village of Uttar Pradesh. Fighting hunger, he eats 'Joothan'. As a school boy, he is made to stand outside the science lab. Tyagi teachers marginalize his educational prospects by assigning him the work of sweeping the class rooms. Sharankumar Limbale too fights hunger and also faces identity crisis. As an illegitimate child, he is neither accepted by his community nor admitted to the family of his upper caste father. Each dalit narrative tells us a heart-rending story that encapsulates harsh realities of life.

In Tamil Nadu, dalit writing came into being nearly two decades after the Marathi Dalit movement. Tamil Dalit writing also has its major influence from the 'Self-respect Movement' started by Ramaswamy Naicker (Periyar) who championed the cause of the underprivileged through his anti-caste and anti-religious propaganda. Bama's *Karukku* (1992), a Tamil autobiography, talks about the repressive caste system in the Christian convent and criticizes the church as a patriarchal agency. Her *Sangati* (1994) as a narrative of polyphony accommodates the voices of several people to make it an autobiography of her community. Bama expresses a different view about church in *Vanmam* (2002). In fact, she appreciates Christianity for bettering the lives of the downtrodden. She attributes the change of her thought to the ongoing dalit movements.

Siddalingaiah's *Orukeri,* a Kannada dalit autobiography, is a comic portrayal of dalit suffering. On the surface, the problem seems to be of humorous kind but its undercurrents are serious. Humorous portrayal of the self by Siddalingaiah is distinguished from other dalit writers.

A recently published Telugu dalit autobiography, *My Father*

Baliah (2011), challenges village feudal system which exploited the lower order in general and the social life of the author's ancestors in particular. Probably this autobiography is the first of its kind to be directly written in English by the author while most of other life narratives were first written in the Indian languages and were translated into English later. No dalit narratives are written without portraying poverty and caste discrimination as entrenched constituents of marginality. These different texts produced by the writers who belong to different sub-categories of the dalit community foreground lived experiences of the whole community. Low caste stigma still affects their lives in every sphere of human society which marginalizes and undermines their achievement and deprives them of social recognition. They portray not just their social victimization but also express their strong voice for equal rights and opportunities and also highlight their creative ability and imaginative power. They claim and prove that they are second to no other community in the creative world.

IV

Caste system is an age-old social phenomenon that gripped the country for centuries and it also segregated a section of people from the mainstream social life. Manu's legislation became a perennial bane to the former untouchables known as dalits today.

Under article 355 of the Indian Constitution, reservations were provided to Scheduled Castes and Scheduled Tribes in employment and education in the backdrop of their socio-economic conditions. In the beginning, this arrangement was made for a period of ten years. From the date of its implementation, amendments to the above article continued with the first one in 1959 and another amendment was made after a period of ten years. With the final amendment in 2000, reservations are still continuing. The government was of the view that a period of ten years intended for implementation of reservations did not bring development of SCs and STs at expected levels. The Government extended the reservation for a period of another ten years taking into consideration the demand made by the reserved classes. The ruling class-elites created an impression that they were committed to the upliftment of the downtrodden. It was sheer vote-bank politics. Caste has become a yardstick for reservation policy in India. It mandated amelioration of the oppressed conditions of the dalits. Dr. B.R. Ambedkar's social movements against caste system and his demand for special privileges for dalits prompted implementation of reservation. There are innumerable castes in India with sub-castes lying under each of the main caste.

In the context of erstwhile Andhra Pradesh, Madiga Dandora Movement was launched with a demand for classification of reservation among dalit sub-caste groups. It is identified that they are more than 60 sub-castes within the dalit community. Malas and Madigas are two important castes with their respective sub-castes known as dependent castes which include Relli, Arundatiya, Baindla, Camar Mochi, Dakkali, Mang, Matangi, Jambavas etc., being categorized under Madiga caste while Adi-Andhra, Aremala, Byagara, Gosangi, Mahar, Maladasu, Mala Jangam etc., are sub-castes of the Mala community. These different sub-castes were listed in the report of the Lakur Committee which was constituted in 1965 by the Government of India to revise the lists of the Scheduled Castes and Scheduled Tribes. A proposal came before the Lakur Committee for de-scheduling relatively advanced communities. 'Mala' community prominently figured in the list. State governments and affected communities strongly represented in favour of retention of various communities in the Schedule. It is construed that Mala community was identified as an advanced community fifty years back. Because of the political interventions, such communities still remain in the lists.

The Madiga Dandora Movement under the aegis of Mr. Mandakrishna Madiga intensified its demand for democratic distribution of the reservation benefits among the dalit Sub-castes based on their population. As a response, the Chandra Babu Naidu Government constituted a one-man Commission headed by the retired justice Ramachandra Raju through its G.O. M.S. No. 99 Social Welfare (J-1) Department dated 10-09-1996, to look into the facts whether the reservation benefits were properly distributed among the target groups within the dalit community or any Sub-caste(s) are enjoying the benefits disproportionate to their population, and even suggested measures to be taken up in the direction of equal distribution of the benefits.

The Ramachandra Raju Commission gave a notification in public media including the Gazette seeking appeals from the individuals and the Heads of Institutions. The Commission procured data/ statistics on various appointments made in different departments by the Service Commissions from 1990 onwards. After its enquiry from all angles, the Commission submitted its report to the Cabinet Sub-Committee on 28.05.1997. The Cabinet Sub-Committee, after its thorough study, approved several recommendations made in the Ramachandra Raju Commission. The then Government approved the recommendations of the Commission and the findings of the Cabinet Sub-Committee as well. The government found that Malas and Adi-Andhras have received reservation benefits disproportionate to their respective population while the Madiga group with Relli as sub-caste did not have adequate representation in Government appointments in tune with its population.

The Commission classified all the sub-castes into four groups for the convenience of reservation benefits: Relli-A with 1%, Madigas-B with 7%; Malas-C with 6% and Adi-Andhras-D with 1% based on their population. Justice Mehra Commission, constituted in 2008 by the then Government, recorded the size of population of different sub-caste groups based on the data submitted by various departments. As per the 2001 statistics, Madiga population constituted 60.74 lakh, Malas 51.39 lakh while

Relli and Adi-Andhras constituted 1.21 lakh and 1.42 lakh respectively. The representation of Madigas in Government Institutions is 31%, while Malas represent 61.8%; Relli and Adi-Andhras represent 0.25% and 2.77 respectively.

It is clear that the representation of Malas at all levels of employment is high and is disproportionate to their population. Most parts of Rayalaseema and Coastal Andhra are concentrated with more Mala population than Madigas while most of the districts have more Madigas than Malas in Telangana State. The Mahabubnagar district in the state tops in the Madiga population. In socio-economic terms, most of the Andhra-Madigas are much better than Telangana Madigas and Malas as well. It is because of abundant natural sources available to them while the Telangana people of the lower category experienced slavish conditions because of rampant bonded labour tradition unleashed by the Nizam regime. They were not exposed to education while the Andhra dalits were blessed with the Christian Missionary education because of the British regime.

We cannot ignore the difference in occupational patterns between Madigas and Malas. Madigas were involved in skinning dead animals and tanning their hides while Malas were village messengers and were involved in weaving. The ancestral calling of Madigas was prone to severe untouchability while the occupation of Malas was less contemptuous. In fact, Andhra Malas and Madigas are dominant groups when compared to Telangana Madigas and Malas; while Malas are more dominant than Madigas in Andhra Pradesh. Despite the hierarchy within, the main contention continued only between Malas and Madigas as a whole. Thus, both of them have become warring groups. They are equally responsible for the betrayal of reservation benefits to their sub-categories which are treated as untouchables among untouchables.

The National Commission for Scheduled Castes, on the strength of facts on record, was of the view that Article 16 (4) of the Constitution of India is an enabling provision; it enables the State to provide the reservation in appointments and also decide how reservation has to be provided. Referring to the judgement of the Hon'ble High Court of Rajasthan, the Commission recommended that the erstwhile Government of Andhra Pradesh might adopt the aforesaid provision and advised further that "educationally and socially most backward castes of the (erstwhile) Andhra Pradesh listed under the Presidential Orders, viz. "Madiga, Relli and Adi-Andhra" may be given proportionate share in the reservation in the State of (erstwhile) Andhra Pradesh only." The then Government initiated implementation of Commission's suggestions in both recruitment and promotions. As a result, Madigas, in particular, got wider chances and some of the Madiga employees also got quick promotions to higher positions. Aggrieved Malas could not digest this fact and pondered over legal possibilities to check this change. As part of this, one Sri E.V. Chennaiah moved the Supreme Court of India against the judgement of High Court of (erstwhile) Andhra Pradesh in which the Scheduled Castes Act, 2000 (Rationalization of Reservation) was upheld. The Supreme Court of India in its judgement dated 5.11.2004 set aside the Andhra Pradesh Scheduled Castes Act, 2000 (Rationalization of Reservation) citing two grounds. First: apportionment of reservation to the SCs and the sub-caste groups cannot be done by the State Legislature; only the Parliament is competent to do so, second: Even Parliament doesn't have the power to do so since Constitution has intended that SCs and STs are individual homogeneous entities. To quote Lakur's report submitted to the Government of India in 1965, "The Scheduled Tribes can also be generally ascertained by the fact that they live apart in hills, and even where they live on the plains, they lead a separate, excluded existence. They are not fully assimilated in the main body of the people. Scheduled Tribes may belong to any religion. They are listed as Scheduled Tribes because of the kind of life led by them (6-7, Revision of the Lists of Scheduled Castes and Scheduled Tribes). Scheduled Castes have been victims of untouchability and caste system while the STs have not grappled with that type of terrible scenario. Theirs is a different case altogether as rightly pointed out in the Lakur report.

Though SCs and STs are homogeneous in their individual entities, as the Supreme Court pointed out, there exist many socio-economic hierarchies and cultural disparities among various castes, sub-castes and tribes. Strictly speaking, the socio-economic conditions of SCs and all STs are not same though they are scheduled in the Indian Constitution as homogeneous entities. Their economic conditions are heterogeneous and even precarious in the case of those living in agency areas and they are certainly different from those living in plains. These imbalances need constitutional rectification and revision of reservation benefits for equal social justice. The decisions of the Schedule Caste Commission appear institutionalizing the constitutional benefits only for one or two dominant sub-categories within the community. Its recommendations for popular schemes for the sub-caste groups appear to be unfair. Instead, the Commission needs to reorganize the constitutionally accrued benefits to the needy groups within the community.

Justice Usha Mehra Committee too found that one or two sub-castes were benefitting from the reservations and all other sub-castes were deprived of the legitimate reservation benefits. The Committee was of the view that States have no power for classification of Sub-Castes. So, the Committee recommended that an amendment be brought to the Constitution of India by adding the sub-clause to the Article 341 (3) intended for classification of the Sub-Castes within the dalit community. But the SC Commission in its meeting held on 21-10-2008 under the chair of Dr. P.L. Punia, felt that recommendation of Justice Usha Mehra Commission regarding Sub-Categorization of SCs into the A, B, C and D groups was not acceptable. The SC Commission referred to the judgement of the Rajasthan High Court in the matter of Akhila Bharatiya Mahasabha vs National Commission for Scheduled Castes and the State of Rajasthan.

The SC Commission suggested that the State Government should devise a proper mechanism to empower the poorest of the poor SCs (in the context of Karamcharis) through free education, establishing or promoting residential schools in every district and reimbursement of self-financing courses. This was thought to be applicable to the Mala-Madiga issue in the erstwhile Andhra Pradesh. It is construed that the SC Commission was in favour of popular schemes for the poor dalits. Malas are opposed to the sub-categorization from the beginning and they caution that any act of sub-categorization would amount to disunity among the dalits. It may not be true because Backward Classes are also categorized into the A, B, C and D for reservation. Despite this classification, they are united as backward classes and they are now popularly known as *Bahujans*. So, why can't classification be possible in the context of dalit sub-categories across the country in general, and Telangana and Andhra Pradesh in particular? Sub-categorization is a precondition and it is warranted for equal distribution of the reservation benefits. It is an inclusive measure towards socio-economic justice.

No social justice would be meaningful without economic justice. As of now, 'caste,' in terms of its oppressive nature, is considered for reservation. Within the oppressed castes, a demand is set for sub-categorization based on population. Reservations, no doubt to say, created a 'class' among various sub-castes through sixty years of constitutional privileges. Reservations cannot be done away with overnight as they are potential political vote-bank. This constitutional relief is intended to propitiate the raging Dalits and also to postpone or avoid political power for them. For horizontal distribution of constitutional benefits, economic conditions should be a strong criterion rather than just caste or population.

It is because a dominant few, who have been accustomed to enjoying reservation benefits for years together, will be the ultimate beneficiaries in the name of majority population. To thwart this phenomenon, actual economic conditions of an oppressed person even within the same community should be a yardstick for proper economic distribution which would surely promote and propel their social and cultural development. Anticipated backlash by the dominant dalit groups in the face of sub-classification or any such measure proving inconvenient to them, the rulers adopt diplomatic role in their initiative for amendments. Constitution of various committees by the governments to study issues, though understood on the surface, would be a case in point.

The external and the internal enemies have been plundering reservation benefits for years. The external enemies are non-dalits who have infiltrated into the dalit domain with their fake certificates are silently grabbing the constitutional benefits meant for the target groups. No dalit group is serious about it. And the internal enemy is within the community. This internal enemy further constitutes two types, one that enjoys the reservation benefits repeatedly and another is a group of religious converts who come under BC(C)/OBC group. They continue to tap the benefits despite a change in their socio-economic status or religious belief through conversion, thus depriving the marginalized sub-castes of the legitimate benefits. These two enemies do not want to be socially known as schedules castes. The external enemy is taking advantage given the perennial conflict between two dominant sub-castes known as Malas and Madigas. The enemy within is more dangerous than the one that has infiltrated into the constitutional benefits. It is no use of blaming others for disunity and oppression being pervasive through the body of sub-caste hierarchy. The internal imbalances must be addressed first at least by classifying the reservation benefits through constitutional amendments. This would be a (temporary) panacea for the boiling issue.

Dalit literature as a genre evolved and flourished in the postcolonial period despite its roots being traced back to Bhakti movement in medieval period. Social movements of Jotiba Phule and B.R. Ambedkar inspired Marathi young dalit writers. With a revolutionary spirit they produced powerful writings ranging from poetry to autobiography in dalit aesthetics and deliberately countered the traditional writing in terms of form and expression. They tried to subvert the rigours of canonical writing and upheld the literature that encapsulated virtues like liberty, equality and fraternity. In every form of literary writing produced by them, dalit intellectuals attempted to contest marginality and resisted caste humiliation perpetrated by the dominant upper castes. Apart from contribution being made by the progressive upper castes to the body of the dalit literature, a treasure of protest writing is being created in several Indian languages by dalits themselves. In this changing literary scenario, dalit writers have carved a niche on the world literary map through innumerable translations in English and other European languages. Now a dalit writer reaches a stage where s/he can see himself/herself declare as a subject of protest but not as an object of pity. Dalits are successfully conquering the socio-economic and cultural marginality through a strong assertion of political identity. Dalit literature is not a literature of vengeance but a movement for the collective emancipation of dalits.

Methods and Methodology

Research Methods are the apparatuses and systems for doing research. Research is a term used liberally for any sort of examination that is planned to reveal new facts. The revelation and the formation of information, thus, lie at the core of research which, as Leedy says, is 'a systematic quest for undiscovered knowledge '(89). Nicolas has rightly pointed out the basic of research: "Research is a very general term for an activity that involves finding out, in a more or less systematic way, things you did not know. A more academic interpretation is that research involves finding out about things that no-one else knew either. "It is about advancing the frontiers of knowledge" (7).

In fact, research in social sciences draws on various long-established traditions. Its origins might, for example, be said to lie with Greek philosophers, Plato and Aristotle, who developed the ways of conceptualizing and categorizing knowledge, truth and human experience in the ancient Greece. Fundamentally, social science research is concerned with people and their life contexts, and with philosophical questions relating to the nature of knowledge and truth (epistemology), values (axiology) and being (ontology) which underpin human judgments and activities (1).

Any research needs methods and approaches for conducting it. The current research is conducted in three phases. In the first phase, methodology is applied for doing research and in the second phase data is collected from primary and secondary sources. Fieldwork is taken up in some select districts of Telangana State where the Madiga community is highly concentrated. The present study warrants fieldwork to validate the existing available sources and records of primary and secondary sources. In the third phase, the available or collected data is analyzed systematically.

I have additionally included sections which discuss the hypothetical foundation to inquire about the mindsets that prompt the distinctive ways of completing research analysis and to arrive at conclusions. This chapter attempts to review the nature of research and the methods being used to undertake a variety of investigations relevant to a wide range of subjects in the proposed study on 'Dependent Dalit Communities: Social and Cultural Perspectives of Baindlas, Chindus and Dakkalis in Telangana State'.

Research projects like this have been undertaken in order to explicate a phenomenon or to validate a theory. That is why research methods are the practical techniques which are used to accomplish research. The present study explores the socio-cultural disparities and ritual relationships among dependent castes within the dalit community. It also rediscovers the cultural space of the dependent castes and their social relation with Madigas as patrons. Above all, this research has been carried out on the lines of sociological and anthropological methods.

The word *ethnography* literally means 'writing about people,' and it is the interest in which some would regard as distinctive. It has led to a boom in all sorts of ethnographic varieties over the last 40 years. The distinctive features revolve around the notions of people as *meaning*-makers, around an emphasis on understanding how people *interpret* their worlds, and the need to understand the particular cultural worlds in which people live. They construct and utilize. The particular 'culture' could be a hospital ward (Roth 1963), a school (Woods 1979), or any society (or grouping within society). We can see here the strong links with anthropological traditions.

For some researchers, it can only be a 'proper' ethnography if the researcher is a participant observer in the everyday lives of whichever society or group s/ he is studying. You will, however, find the term ethnography linked to a wide range of studies, not all of which make extensive or even any use of participant observation in the strong sense of the term. However, whether the researcher spends years living with this or that group or is attempting via interviews to access and understand interpretations, it is clear that the researcher as a 'human instrument' brings to bear (unavoidably) his or her own interpretations and cultural orientations into the picture (16).

Ethnography has its beginnings in social human studies, and specifically crafted by Malinowski whose original content *Argonauts of the Western Pacific* (1922) portrays his experience of living for quite a while with South Pacific islanders, and insight the anthropologist to spend no less than a year in the field, to take in the dialect, and to live as one of the populaces which he or she thinks about. The accentuation in ethnography is to concentrate on the whole culture. Initially, the possibility of a culture was attached to the idea of ethnicity and geographic area; however, it has been widened to incorporate essentially any gathering or association. That is, we can contemplate on the way of life, cultural ethos, art and performance of a particular section of society or community.

Ethnography, to a great extent, deals with expansive region with an incredible assortment of experts and strategies. Be that as it may, the most widely recognized ethnographic approach is member perception as pieces of field inquire about. The ethnographer moves towards becoming submerged in the way of life as a functioning member of the society/community where he or she is going to study and records the encompassing field notes related to the study concerned. The present research is basically grounded on the principle of ethnographic investigation. Here ethnographic method has been used to show socio-economic politics of the privileged castes towards lower castes in a very comprehensive manner. The ethnography of performance of Dakkalis and Chindus has been documented and analyzed as to how these dependent castes have been pushed to oblivion with the strong impact of the movies and other electronic media.

People are no more interested in performing such traditional songs due to a blatant onslaught of the commodification of art through electronic means by the privileged sections and the new generation youth are not at all concerned about their rich cultural heritage. Moreover, Governments are least bothered about documenting their traditional/folk repertoire. These dalit artistes belonging to dalit communities are not encouraged from any point of view to promote their cultural legacy through artistic performances. As a result, we are losing the content of such performances day by day. During the field visit, apart from their performance, an informal conversation was conducted to understand the socio-economic and cultural politics of the dalit community.

Participant observation is one of the basic tools for conducting ethnographic research. This method would ensure Madiga community to pick up profound information about the complexities and inward workings that couldn't be possible from writing or a kind of strategy where data is found out second-hand. It yields experiences of the lives of people and their traditions that they would not have the capacity to let you know if you just inquired. The researcher lives inside a specific setting, keeps up associations with individuals, partakes in community ritualistic performance, and expands notes on the experience. It empowers the researcher with explorative knowledge to see the way of life without forcing their own social reality on that particular culture.

Survey methods are a portion of the central techniques for gathering and examining information in sociological and anthropological aspects of research. Survey methods have been used since the beginning. It is being used extensively in a variety of subjects such as key methods in business, government policies, marketing and other connected areas. Survey methods have been utilized all through the world and have turned into a vital reason for the relative social investigation. While the basics of study explore accumulations of organized information as a rule with an organized data and the factual examination of the interrelationships of factors, the act of overview investigation always indicates signs of change.

During the survey, interviews were conducted after performances by the artistes. Selected performers and their household members were interviewed to extract basic information. They were asked about family income source, total number of family members, male-female ratio, education and social status, context of art practice of the particular performance, historical and mythological genealogy of the performance. The survey was conducted a number of times in several villages and mandal headquarters (between 10 July 2017 and 15 May 2018) that covered fifty respondents who belonged to different age groups. The respondents were categorized by their age groups: below 25 years of age, between 25 and 55 years and above. We categorized between performers and non-performers. For collecting data, we prepared questionnaires as part of our current research. Survey method again can be classified into qualitative (open-ended questions) and quantitative (e.g. use yes or no answers) measures.

Survey research has much significance in the 21st century technological world. It was one of the critical research strategies in the past as well. Antiquated rulers used to apply review strategy to know the circumstances in their kingdoms and to evaluate their strategies. With the developing significance for data in the contemporary society, survey has become one of research methods.

With the mechanical headway, the stream of data has been made into a critical part of the contemporary world. That is why the present world is portrayed as the 'Data Society' and we have a problem with the emergence of Big Data in the contemporary society. Consequently, surveys have moved towards a vital part of the present world. The generation and circulation of data turned into an imperative part of monetary framework. An overview is an industry in the cutting-edge world. Survey research is about moderately reasonable and has an alternate method for overseeing the examination to browse. In the light of specialists' prerequisites and confinements, we can lead up close and personal meetings, email interviews and so on. Survey research is ordinarily completed with the assistance of institutionalized survey. So, inquiries wind up in extremely broad terms and they miss what might be most suitable to respondents. Also, the poll ought to stay unaltered all through the examination, which makes a review strategy rigid. The appropriate responses from the respondents shift from the viewpoint of the unique circumstance. Survey research expects to add up to trustworthiness from the members, which is another impediment.

Both essential and optional information have been utilized as part of the research. Broad utilization was made of the administration records, District Gazetteers, Census information on the selected districts of Telangana, the record of specialists' perceptions made in the Baindlas, Chindus and Dakkalis more than two decades throughout the past research work embraced by the scientists, and so forth and counselled books, compilations, diaries, periodicals, articles, sites and different wellsprings of printed and digital material. These instruments helped the researcher in gathering solid information to make the research formulations.

The primary data was collected using an open-ended but structured schedule and focused group, besides shooting the skits and extensive photography, through a field study spreading over a year. The focal point of the field work was to collect the data on the current status of Baindlas, Chindus and Dakkalis, the dependent castes of the Madiga group in Telangana State. An endeavour was additionally made to elicit information on the present performative situation of Dakkalis and Chindus by virtue of the invasion of motion pictures and electronic media. The examination procedure in the field included the sorting out of exhibitions to archive pertinent data and assemble it for this investigation, and was accordingly directed through the accompanying exercises:

- Exhibitions of various communities of the Madiga group were organized.
- Performances through photography and videography were organized.
- Interviews with performers, community members and the audience conducted.
- A primary survey was conducted in the village.

The artistic performances glorifying Madiga culture and narrating legendary stories relating to the local goddesses of the selected three villages were organized. Performances were held in the respective villages to encourage communication with the community and the performers. They were asked to perform '*Chindu Bhagavatam*' and *Dakkalis' Kulapuranam* or *Jambapuranam* based on their caste history. The performances of troupes were observed, documented and explored further on their narrative and theatrical performance style. Conducting and recording informal interviews with performers, community leaders, the villagers and audiences of the village (before and after the performance) was undertaken at the time of the performance.

Marshall and Rossman describe data analysis as the process of bringing order, structure and meaning to the mass of collected data. "It is described as messy, ambiguous, and time-consuming; but also it is a creative and fascinating process" (150). Broadly speaking, while it does not proceed in linear fashion, it is the activity of making sense of, interpreting and theorizing data that signifies a search for general statements among categories of data. That is why we need to follow proper forms or steps to analyze the accumulated data (6). In this context, J.W. Best & Kahn assert:

"the analysis and interpretation of data represent the application of deductive and inductive logic to the research" (354). Antonius succinctly states that "the word data points to information that is collected in a systematic way and organized and recorded to enable the reader to interpret the information correctly" (n.p.).

Collected statistical data would help understand the size of the population of sub-caste/ dependent castes within the dalit communities populated in various districts of the Telangana State. As per the requirement, certain techniques have been adopted to make use of the collected data for critical analysis.

Thus, efforts were made to achieve the objectives of the present study. In the next chapter, the data on Madiga community in some districts of Telangana State has been collected and discussed to draw conclusions. Some recommendations have been for further research studies. Research is always a never-ending process of generating new ideas to the body of existing knowledge. I hope this study will erase the gap pertaining to the Madiga sub-caste communities and it would be resourceful for further studies.

Caste as Identity in Social System

Caste has been institutionalized in Indian society and impacted the social life with its gradation in the status and identity of the people. It also examines its origin and evolution that happened through the ages. Caste as an Indian phenomenon has created a wedge in the social fabric of Indian society. The word 'Casta' is of Spanish and Portuguese origin, which means race or lineage. It is castus in Latin which means pure. It is said that the Spaniards were the first to use it. In the academics, the present spelling of the word 'caste' appeared in French in 1740. Before this time, it was spelt as 'cast.' In Ketkar's words, "'caste' was used in the sense of breed or race in the middle of the sixteenth century" (12).

Darwin applied this word to the different classes of social insects. It is very interesting to look at it in the Indian context: "The caste system was believed to be a divine institution till the British period, and despite resistance from the Dalit-Bahujan masses (SC, ST and OBCs), the hegemonization of Brahminical culture, practice and ritualism has been established through well-designed ideological and political moves. The construction of a purity and pollution theory to examine caste relations is part of this ideological design" (Ilaiah 94).

Kancha Ilaiah is of the view that caste system is a cleverly designed ideological product by Brahmins who claim to be pure while other social groups and the so-called untouchables in particular are polluted. Ilaiah further clarifies that though Luis Dumonth's study of caste system on purity-pollution line continues; his theory states: "Brahminical castes constructed their selves as 'pure' and other castes as 'polluted.'"

Social groups are abiding by a set of certain norms within the group. The community does not transgress the community norms for inter-marriage and inter-dining. Because of this reason, inter-caste marriages and inter-dining arrangements are not allowed between different castes or communities. According to Ram Ahuja, "caste is a closed social stratum that determines its members' prestige, occupation, and social relationships and in each caste, social relations between members of different castes are severely limited and formalized" (240). He means to say that a set of caste norms invariably governs community as a whole where individuals have to abide by them in their marital relations.

There was a misconception about caste as being of divine origin or scriptural origin and its central role was attributed to Manu, the Hindu law-giver. Dismissing the theory of the religious and textual origin of caste, quoting Dr. Baba Saheb Ambedkar, Kannabiran says, "Caste existed long before Manu whose role was limited to codifying existing rules and preaching them" (36). Though Manu was not responsible for invention of caste, he unequivocally strengthened and spread its infection through codification of rules in vogue. Thus, the Hindu spiritual world attributed divinity to caste system:

> There is no doubt to say that caste system has brought a vicious divide in Indian society and created numerous small communities under each caste. Every local unit of a caste has its own peculiar customs and a regulating internal mechanism. Each caste is sub-divided into small groups being delimited on matrimonial dimensions. Members of each caste believe that they have a common ancestor being real or mythical personage. Inter-marriages between them are considered as incest. Because of this reason, they marry outside the group within the sub-caste. According to Ekta Singh, "The sub-castes generally resemble the caste in being endogamous for marriage to anyone other than a member of the same sub-caste is unlawful. On the other hand the innermost group which is known by various names (such as *gotra, got, kul*) is exogamous." (28)

It is clear that basically caste is responsible for further creation of sub-castes and groups. Caste serves as an outer layer while sub-caste operates as an inner layer. In fact, sub-caste originates from caste itself. Both of them have their own socio-cultural limitations. They are endogamous in nature. Transgression of matrimonial limits would not only be unlawful but would invoke excommunication from the caste or sub-caste group. For example, Madiga is a caste while Baindla or Dakkali is a sub-caste in Telangana state. Madigas do not accept matrimonial alliance either from Baindla or from Dakkali sub-caste. In the same way, Dakkali too does not allow marriage of their bride with the bridegroom of Baindla sub-caste. It is due to occupational variations and also internal regulations which form a separate group with an identity which is different from other groups. But both the sub-castes have roots in Madiga which is a patron-caste while other two are termed dependent castes. Quoting Blunt, G.S. Ghurye says, "So-called sub-castes, which are really castes of the first grade, degree and stage, are not fissions but fusions" (195). As far as Dr. Karve's view, quoted by Ghurye, is concerned, "sub-caste" is a grouping known to the people of the caste while caste is the grouping known to society at large." This statement can be substantiated with the existing situation among the castes and sub-castes. For example, Dakkali, Chindu, Baindlas and Dasari, are dependent castes affiliated to Madigas and Malas respectively. Ekta Singh says, "The fission of castes into sub-castes is due to many causes. One of the most frequent criterions is the adoption of different occupation. It is common for the members of a caste, who sell an article to separate from, and claim superiority to those who produce it. "Division is caused. Different social customs make divisions, for example, those who prohibit the remarriage of widows and those who permit it to form separate sub-caste" (28).

Adoption of occupation, though a major cause to decide the social status of a person, will not change the rigidity of one's caste as it is socially attributed. For example: if a Dakkali, a lower caste person takes to the profession of priesthood, he/she will not be treated as a Brahmin. Irrespective of his occupation, he is known as Dakkali by birth. So, ultimately birth would be a criterion to determine one's caste not occupation.

Given the fundamental principle, caste is associated with endogamy and heredity. The nature of endogamy is narrow and its scope is limited. For example, a man must marry a woman of his own caste. Endogamy prescribes stringent principles and obligations in marital contexts, and also it regulates marriage system within the established tradition. People of that particular social group cannot violate the *sapinda* rule. In the broader sense, Indian society is characterized by an elaborate custom of exogamy. This rule prohibits marriage between *sapindas* and *sagotras* (Sagotra is a compound word, a union of *sa* and *gotra*, meaning the same clan).

The rule of exogamy is rigid and its violation invites rigorous penalties. The principle of endogamy is overlaid against the exogamous society. In caste endogamy, a homogeneous population is split into mutually exclusive units in which both the principles of endogamy and exogamy keep operating in all their rigidity and stringency. Thus, endogamy promotes caste rigidity and creates environment for caste severity in its practice.

Caste is understood to have been created through superimposition of endogamy on exogamy. The rule of exogamy enabled flexibility in the institution of marriage outside one's caste. It is one of the possible views about creation of caste. But there is another view that relates to sex ratio. According to Kannabiram, "some complex rules about marriage must have been in place, which must have taken into account the sex ratio among persons of marriageable age from marriageable groups within a caste" (36). The imbalance of sex ratio arises from the death of a spouse within a caste: "surplus women" and "surplus men." This creates imbalance in sex ratio. The rule of exogamy removes imbalances of sex ratio and ensures equity among various sex groups by virtue of its effective practice.

To redress the problem of 'surplus' in a crude manner, the surplus woman was proposed either to be burnt on her husband's funeral pyre or was subjected to enforced widowhood while surplus man could not be burnt on the funeral pyre of his wife because he was a man. He could not be condemned to celibacy, simply because he was an asset to the group. This was an open gender discrimination which was accepted by the society. Rajasthan's incident of 'sati' was a case in point.

Caste in India is a pervasive phenomenon that affected attitudes, beliefs, and behaviour of the members of the Hindu religion. The caste phenomenon leads Indians into different social and cultural groups prone to social disintegration. Other religions too imitated the Hindu social practice. Conversions to non-Hindu religions failed to curb the caste discrimination and religious prejudice. This cancerous disease spread across all religions even though religions like Islam and Christianity claim that they are free from caste system and equality of human beings is the innate spirit of their religions.

In Sonnad's words, "it is so entrenched that the features of the caste system can be found among members of other religious castes in India" (117). It is unfortunate that such universal religions are riddled with caste system and its consequent effects are discernible in social and cultural fabric. Hindus are active carriers and transmitters of caste-virus. Caste system continues to exist with them wherever they go and settle. Indians living abroad are no exception. It has become a global phenomenon with the spread of Hindu population. An average Hindu individual riddled with the caste problem is an effective carrier even to the remotest foreign lands and other human spheres.

Varna would basically mean colour. Varna system was in vogue for centuries in the Indian social milieu. Hindus were categorized into four major divisions: Brahman, Kshatriya, Vaisya, and Sudra. Brahmins are the priestly class and Kshatriyas are the warrior class. Vaisyas are the merchant class while Sudras are the working class meant to serve other three classes/ varnas. The Hindu scholars prescribed obligations and duties in tune with the social gradation in the Varna system which became the fountain source of hundreds and thousands of sub-divisions being called *jatis* and sub-castes.

The terms caste and *jati* may be synonymously used. Each of the four divisions of the Hindu Varna comprises hundreds of sub-categories or sub-castes. *Jati,* which is an Indian word, would also mean 'class,' a social group with similar linguistic and cultural characters. There is also a *panchama* category which is outside the Varna system though it is an integral part of the Hindu religious customs, traditions and cultural practices. There are several Sanskrit words attributed to this category. Their nomenclatures are different from one another but their essential function is same. *Panchamas* are untouchables who have no place within the Varna ladder. Practice of caste or *jati* is pervasive in Indian society. In the western context, *jati* would mean race—Whites and Blacks. Colour discrimination generated a stigma of apartheid in America where Africans are treated as inferior to the White people. In the same way, the African Americans are looked down upon by Americans: "The race relations between Whites and African Americans in the United States in the past have been described as a caste system based on a rigid hereditary demarcation, prohibition of intermarriage between two groups, and limited social mobility for the minorities" (117).

In history, Americans enslaved Blacks on colour lines. In America, apartheid still continues in one form or the other, though this discriminatory treatment is legally punishable. In India, there is no colour discrimination but social discrimination is practiced based on one's caste which is ascribed on lines of ancestral callings and occupations. There is also hierarchy in the occupational patterns. For example, a shoe-maker or tanner is treated as socially lowly due to the so-called degraded occupation which is ascribed by birth. It is a crude social tradition of the Indian varna system.

Jati would also mean 'tribe.' For example, *Konda-jati*, a hill-tribe, comprises a group of people living on the high hills or in deep forests with their similar traditions and customs. Konda Reddis constitute a tribal group which is more backward than any other tribal unit in Khammam district of Telangana state. Though most of the tribal groups live outside the mainstream social life, they are not branded as untouchables. Thay have no stigma of purity-pollution. They have their customs and traditions distinct from that of the mainstream society. However, tribal employees living in towns and cities have no different life from that of the Hindu mainstream society. They are integrated into the Hindu society and worship Hindu gods.

Following is the scheduled list of sub-castes under Madiga community. 18 sub-castes are listed with allotted serial number against each. Among those listed the reasons for selecting dependent castes like Baindlas, Dakkalis and Chindus is that these dependent castes are closely associated with Madiga community being the patron class for them.

The Ramachandra commission constituted by the then government of the united Andhra Pradesh identified the sub-castes under Madiga category of the Scheduled Castes.

Madiga Sub-Castes

Allotted Serial No.	Name of Sub-Caste
5	Arundhateeya
9	Beda Jangam, Budaga Jangam
10	Baindla
14	Chamar, Mochi, Machee
15	Chamar
17	Dakkal, Dokkalwar
19	Dhoor
24	Godari

28	Jaggali
29	Jambhawulu
30	Kolupulawandlu
32	Madiga
33	Madigadasu, Masthin
43	Mang
44	Mang Garodi
47	Maatangi
56	Samagara
59	Sindhollu, Chindollu/ Chindus

Source: G.O M.S No. 68 dated 6-6-1997 issued by M.S Rajaji, Chief Secretary, Government of the then-Andhra Pradesh, trans. Bheemaiah

Madigas constitute a principal segment of various sub-castes in dalit community. Mala is another caste like Madiga, which is socially, politically dominant in both Telangana State and Andhra Pradesh. As stated earlier, among the 17 sub-castes or *jatis,* Baindla, Chindu and Dakkali are the dependent castes of the Madiga community. *Jambapurana* is a caste myth of Madigas. The myth of lower castes was never made part of the Indian *Ashtadashapuranas*. Kings and emperors glorified the culture of their lineage through *puranas* which served them as vehicles of their fame and name. In the light of this, the Brahminical society negated glorification of the lower order in *puranas* and legends. Labelling *Jambapurana* as a caste myth, Brahmins segregated it from a cluster of the eighteen *puranas*.

Dependent castes began to valorize the Madiga history and culture in order to extricate 'social prestige' of the patrons. It would be a relevant account to discuss the roots of Madiga community to explore the socio-cultural dimensions of the dependent communities. *Jambapurana* is the cultural history of Madiga community. The roots of Madigas can be traced through this text. "Madiga is not a single caste, indeed it is a cluster of castes including many sub-castes. Some critics call them dependent castes while some other prefer the term like 'satellite' castes" (Gurram 116).

Jambapurana is a fountain source of the Madiga culture and history. Emulating upper castes, Madigas too have established their caste identity and social position. In the words of Laban Babu, "Madigas were rulers of various kingdoms in the ancient period. They became Dasyas after they were conquered in their war with the Aryans" (6). *Jambapurana* is a philosophical and literary discourse on the Madiga-Brahmin relationship. Quoting Kanneganti Gopal of Naskal village in Nalgonda district, Gurram Seetaramaulu says, "*Jambapurana* was initially a form of palm leaf manuscript" and it was performed by reading at a later stage with the help of a scroll. Since it was difficult to preserve the scroll for a long period, it was adopted into performance through different art forms. Dakkalis perform through a scroll as a means of narrative telling. The scroll has a number of pictures with their different stills. The narrator is a Dakkali man who explains the story of cultural significance of Madigas. In the words of Jayadhir Thirumala Rao and A.K. Prabhakar, "The performance of Dakkali *Jambapurana* is not known to the outside world as the Dakkalis beg only from Madigas and perform for them citing mythological reasons. They clarified on their traditions and belief systems; they have turned these reasons into their faith" (x).

According to the myth, Jambavamuni was born before creation itself. The birth of Adishakti, Trinities, Kamadhenu, Saraswati, Lakshmi and Parvati took place. According to *Jambapurana*, Jambavas were Madigas who ruled the ancient India which was known as Jambudweepam. Jambava is not the name of a person but the name of the Madiga community. Adi-Jambavas were of the Alastroid origin. They were prosperous and civilized. Madigas claim that they are the children of Jambavantha or Jambavamuni whose legacy has been preserved for centuries. *Jambapuranam* makes a cultural interpretation of Madiga village life. It has been used as a document to represent the Madiga life.

It was considered an alternative history or a cultural narrative meant for Madigas. Now this purana is used for political assertion.

Madigas who enjoyed a great social position and cultural reputation in the past became *dasas*. *Jambapurana* traces how the Madigas were made untouchables. According to the mythical story, "Kamadhenu, the divine cow can feed any number of people. Parvati invites only gods, goddesses and sages to taste its milk and milk products. An adolescent who looks after Kamadhenu feels like tasting the cow's milk. When he expresses his desire to Parvati, she asks him to go and tell this to Kamadhenu. On hearing this desire, the divine cow collapses and dies. All the gods and goddesses eagerly flock for its flesh. Jambavantha and the boy, Chennaiah by name, start cooking the flesh. While stirring it, a piece of flesh falls down from the vessel, Jambavantha and the boy together put it back into the vessel. For this act, they are cursed to be re-born as untouchables on earth. This story provides Madigas with a mythical basis for their 'self-esteem" (130). On the other side, the myth also asserts cultural and social integrity between Malas and Madigas. "The episode of Chennaiah and Jambava, on sharing the Kamadhenu meat, emphasizes the need for bonding between Malas and Madigas. "The idea of social justice emerges from the episode rooted in purana. This can be applied even to the categorization of reservation based on population" (Rao and Prabakar). Categorization of reservation is misunderstood as a divide among dalits in Telugu states. Integrity among various sub-castes including Mala-Madigas should be envisaged and envisioned not just in terms of political slogans but in terms of the equal distribution of economic benefits based on population of the sub-caste communities. This is one strong demand. But there is another aspect which may demand distribution of reservation fruits based not on population but majorly on economic conditions among various sub-cates within the dalit community. This should be the crux of the reservation enshrined in the Indian constitution.

This may not be compatible for majority reserved categories in the country. It is because reservation is such a constitutional relief which is extracted more by the dominant groups and less or nothing by the weaker or unnoticed groups. This would be a repetitional exercise by the dominant beneficiaries. Achievement of equal economic justice is to remain only as a slogan but never has it gone into effect.

Madigas claim their cultural past which is substantiated through *Jambapurana* and the stories of Arundathi. There is evidence in the *Ramayana* and the *Bhagavata* that Rama and Krishna too had relations with Jambavantha. It is construed that no other sub-caste in the dalit community had such a great cultural legacy as the Madigas. Jambavantha is said to be born as a bear from the Brahmin's yawn. There are innumerable references given about Jambavantha through Kritha and Dwapara yugas. Jambavantha threw his presence during the churning of the sea and also during the incarnation of Vamana as well. He stood by Rama in wars. He married off his daughter, Jambavathi to Krishna and also gifted him *Shyamanthakamani* a precious stone in his daughter's marriage. Jambavantha is frequently depicted as a prudent veteran in the episodes of *Sundarakanda* and *Yudhakanda* of the *Ramayana.* When all were anxious about the abducted Sita, he was the one who recommended the name of Hanuman for his ability to solve the problem. He was a wise person who was aware of the capabilities of Hanuman. "Without hesitation, Jambavantha was given a significant place in the traditional *purana* for his merit" (Laban 17).

Indian literary history has failed to adequately record the life of women communities lying unrecognized at the bottom of society in the dalit world. Among those neglected are the Madiga sub-castes whose life is yet to be touched upon in the Telugu literary domain. Caste-based society in India has never recognized the productive castes whose contribution to the growth of the Indian economy is tremendous. There exist about eighteen

Madiga sub-castes under sixty-two sub-castes of dalit community in Telangana and Andhra Pradesh. The miseries of these sub-castes have not been adequately textualized. The caste pyramid, which has its strong roots in the Varna system, created a vertical order even among the lower castes. In this socially sub-categorized hierarchy, a sub-caste of the same community looks down upon the other. Within the dalit community, Madiga is one principal sub-caste which looks down upon its dependent castes like dakkali. Ironically Madigas are also looked down upon by Malas, a dominant dalit community. All the sub-castes of dalit community are discriminated against by the caste Hindus in the country.

During the Nizam's regime in the Hyderabad Presidency, all the lower castes including dalits served the Nizam village official machinery. The Nizam regime imposed bonded labour against the working class. Police Patels and Mali Patels maintained the law and order in villages and collected revenue from the people. Madigas were assigned to carry post from one village to another village or police station. As a rule, they were bound to carry a faggot along with the post to hand it over to the addressee. They would get nothing in return but shoe-blows. A man or woman from each family of the lower communities was compelled to render bonded labour. Dalits being landless poor made a major contribution to the village development.

Dominant upper castes are well aware of the fact that Dalits being the productive classes could bring any kind of land under cultivation. Every caste Hindu knows their agrarian capabilities. In recognition of the collective labour, the *Nizam Sarkar* granted gifted waste lands for cultivation known as Maanyam lands. These lands remained in the joint possession of Madigas and other dependent castes like Dakkalis and Chindus at many places of Telangana. Since Dakkalis and Chindus are nomadic and dependent castes, they had no idea of agriculture. The 'caste accord' also confined them to singing and narrating the legends of the Madiga life and culture. Within the colony, Madiga families are classified based on their ancestral lineage. Each Madiga lineage has several families. Each lineage group is represented by the Madiga chief and Maanyam land is cultivated in rotation by the respective families. The Madiga cultivator is bound to offer 'Maanyam' to Dakkalis in lieu of the part of Maanyam land given to the former. Two Madiga short stories are taken from a Telugu anthology, *Nallaregati Sallu* (Furrows of the Black Soil), to understand the relation between Madigas and the dependent castes. The title of this anthology is symbolic, in the sense that life of the marginalized is linked to agricultural land. Majority of the marginalized sections rely on physical labour. No furrows are possible on farms without their toil. Jupaka Subhadra's *Maanyam* and Gogu Shyamala's *Thataki* represent two different sub-castes which deal with the question of land rights, one of the major issues connected with the lives of the vulnerable. *Maanyam* portrays the rights of Dakkalis over 'Maanyam' land and also their relationships with Madigas while *Thataki* delineates how an attempt is made to seize back the land which was granted to the Madiga family under the land ceiling act three generations ago. The issue revolves round land rights. It also discusses the relationships of Madigas with the dominant upper castes in rural Telangana. The two stories also discuss how social relationships are maintained among the lower castes and their relationships with the upper castes. Jupaka Subhadra and Gogu Shyamala, being insiders, write the stories of the Madiga life and culture in Telugu with Madiga consciousness. They are part of the vulnerable village life. Characters deployed in their stories are not fictitious. They are real characters. Their stories are replete with the real incidents. The characters pour out their lived experiences. Their portrayal is natural and it is wrought in the jargon of the illiterate Madiga sub-castes of Telangana state.

Dakkali men are artistes by profession, whose livelihood is precarious. They do not have fixed settlements. They are nomadic and keep on moving from village to village throughout the year. Dakkalis live in makeshift shacks under trees on the fringes of the Madiga colonies. Their traditional claim is that they are born from the ribs of Madigas and thus they declare themselves to be their slaves. They also lay a claim for entitlement to food and 'Maanyam' from the Madiga families in lieu of their land given to them for cultivation. They are bound to beg for food only from the Madiga families. "They share with the platter but not with the bed". This indicates their slavish relation with the patron community. To understand the social relations between patrons and the dependent castes, a Dakkali story is drawn in this context.

Rayakka, the protagonist in the story, *Maanyam,* is affectionately addressed by Madigas. In the beginning of the story, we notice her stepping into the village called Damaranchalapally in Warangal district of Telangana State. She decides to stay in the village for fifteen days in order to claim her 'Maanyam.' Though Madigas socially look down upon Dakkalis, cordial relations are maintained with the dependent castes. Muganna, a Madiga, affectionately accosts Rayakka and enquires about her well-being and that of her family members. He forges sisterly relations with Dakkali Rayakka. The writer, Jupaka Subhadra, too addresses Rayakka as Rajakka in her story. In fact, marital relations do not exist between Dakkalis and Madigas but their mutual addresses indicate a kind of 'affection' regardless of sub-caste hierarchy.

The story goes further that a man belonging to the Mala caste is fascinated by the serpentine beauty of Rayakka. He breaks the caste rule of endogamy and joins her life. He is a layman to the Dakkali profession. Rayakka tells stories with the help of other Dakkali men and narrates *Jambapurana* that glorifies the Madiga culture. She knows how to ward off evil by tying amulets to the sick. According to the caste accord, Dakkalis are entitled to food twice a day from the Madiga families. In fact, they act as media for Madigas. They act as the spokespersons of the Madiga culture. Rayakka's father shared with her half of the forty villages as an offer of bride-price. She is capable of arbitrating disputes between Madigas and Dakkalis.

Once Rayakka suffers and expresses her anguish for not receiving her share of 'Maanyam.' She also complains to the Madiga chief about the denial of her legitimate share from Muttanna who is supposed to offer it in lieu of her Maanyam land. On Rajakka's complaint, the Madiga chief looks into the issue. In his enquiry, he comes to know the simple reason that Muttanna is also not allowed by his own brother, Mysanna, to cultivate the land through the year. So, he is unable to share the paddy with Rayakka. Maisanna's response is that his brother did not give him money after selling some babul trees which are part of Maanyam land. Muttanna admits that due to some financial problems, he spent money. Rayakka who is well aware of the complexity of the problem sets a condition to both the Madiga brothers in a way that she should be given either her share of grain or pay the fine in case of failure. She applies her wisdom for the amicable settlement of the dispute. Rayakka is deployed as the protagonist of the story. Thus, the female character is empowered and given a due place.

Thataki is a story that portrays how Tirumal Rao, the Karnam Dora of the village, attempts to seize the land back from Basaiah. The beneficiary Basaiah's grandfather, Eeraiah, a farm labourer, was gifted the land by Venkat Rao, Tirumal Rao's grandfather, during the Bhoodhan Movement. Venkat Rao thought that his farm labourer would never be able to cultivate it and at any time the land would be taken back from him. He wanted to earn fame as a champion of the cause of the landless poor. But his plans were upset by the government bringing this land under ceiling.

Balamma, the daughter of Basaiah, is a girl of twelve. She is shrewd, courageous and heroic. She takes care of her ground-nut field whenever her father is away. Once, her father admiringly makes remarks, "My father is reborn as Balamma" (34). Balamma, in her teens, is work-minded and punctual. No boy of her age can match her in her work. Yellaiah and Narsaiah are addressed as *Yelladu* and *Narsadu* out of affection by the elders and other peer groups. Upper castes intentionally address the lower castes with derogatory suffixes by way of perpetuating cultural humiliation and oppression of Dalits. For instance, Thirumala Rao Dora addresses Basaiah as 'Bashega' or Bashya to mean that the man is untouchable who does not deserve his original name but the twisted one. Thus, they twist the name to lower their social status. In contrast, the lower castes are invariably bound to address the dominant upper castes as 'doras' or 'patels'. Lower castes have to glorify the dominant upper castes in every way.

In her routine, Balamma wets her ground-nut field at dawn, thinking that others might deprive her of legitimate share of water by over-using it. In her naiveness, she asserts her rights to equal share of water for her field. This enrages Tirumal Dora who calls her Tataki to mean a 'mischief.' In Telugu local dialect, a mischievous woman is generally termed as 'Tataki.' In the *Ramayana*, Tataki is projected as a demon. Gogu Shyamala subverts the negative image and deploys Tataki in her story as a heroine. She identifies Balamma with Tataki. She deconstructs the Hindu culture and the dominant attitude over the marginalized sections, she attempts to reconstruct the Madiga culture with a positive image of characters. Shyamala deliberately says 'yes.' Balamma is Tataki in the positive terms of her acumen, intelligence and bravery. She kicks on the private parts of the Dora who slaps her cheek and even makes a vain bid to rape her. Her bold resistance is suggestive of her courage and heroism.

Tirumal Dora plans to eliminate Balamma's father in order to grab the land. He avoids inviting Basaiah and his daughter to the public gathering for an amicable settlement of the land in a democratic way. He drags Balamma into the *jawar* fields while working alone. In arrogance, he takes law into his hands. Due to his atrocious behaviour, the girl undergoes a painful experience. In *Maanyam*, Rayakka complains to the Madiga chief when

Muttaiah denies her the legitimate share of paddy. But Muttaiah does not commit any atrocity against Rayakka like Tirumal Dora. The problem is settled amicably. These incidents testify to the fact that the relations between lower caste groups are cordial and democratic while the relations between lower castes and upper castes are often prone to conflicts due to caste oppression and religious prejudice.

When Tirumal Dora holds her arm, she is surprised because upper caste people generally don't touch the untouchables. She comes to know that he is Tirumal Dora of the neighbouring field. In grappling with him, she yells for help and pleads with him to let her go. He arrogantly calls her a 'base born.' He further abuses her saying, "Are you a small child? What is it that you have lost here and engaged in watering the field like a man? Do Malas and Madigas not have brains to keep their female children at home?" For Tirumal Dora, the question of sharing water for his field is just a pretext. Actually, he has decided to seize the land back by threatening the Basaiah family. He even goes to the extent of eliminating Basaiah at any moment. He realizes that his evil deed would easily come out and he would get into trouble. He shifts his plan from eliminating Basaiah to atrocity against his daughter.

There could be conflicting incidents even among the lower castes but there is no element of savagery in them. Dakkali Rayakka's issue is a case in point. Rayakka never indulges in violence though she is denied her share of Maanyam. Madiga Pochavva refuses to offer food to Rayakka who is not done any harm by her refusal. In the same way, the response of the two brothers to Rayakka is not atrocious. She asserts her legitimate rights and fights with Madigas within the democratic framework. Rayakka's complaint to the Madiga chief would mean that she wants justice subject to caste accord. But the same attitude is not noticed in Tirumal Dora who breaks the natural principle of justice in solving the problem because he belongs to the dominant upper caste community. His decision is arbitrary and harmful in nature which results in the atrocity against the innocent girl.

These two stories are concrete examples of how the marginalized sections of society struggle for their survival due to conflicts with the upper castes. *Maanyam* is a powerful Madiga-Dakkali story that delineates power structure and cultural variations within the community. Caste hierarchy defines the power structure in different terms. “Madiga caste accord” which is still in practice would strengthen the endogamous marital alliances in the community on one hand and breaks the endogamous norm with a Dakkali woman marrying a Mala man. In *Thataki*, the Hindu dominant culture represented by Tirumal Rao is subverted and the culture of productive castes represented by the Balamma family is valorized. The writer sustains her argument in favour of the land rights of dalits. Demolition of sub-caste hierachial structures within the dalit community would pave the way for collective liberation from the upper caste oppressive practices.

Baindlas as Priestly Community

Caste is categorized into innumerable sub-castes; the caste groups are not aware of this complexity in Indian society. There are dependent castes which exist at the bottom of the society. According to the Ramachandra Raju commission, there are about more than sixty sub-castes within the dalit community in Telangana. Dependent castes like Baindlas, Chindus and Dakkalis are artistes who figure prominently on the schedule. Baindlas, due to caste-based occupation, are a priestly class within the dalit community to negotiate rituals and marriage ceremonies for Madigas who are termed as a patron community. The traditional instruments the Baindlas use while conducting ceremonial functions and religious acts are symbolic of their social category and priestly role. Yellamma is the village local deity worshipped by Madigas and other innumerable marginalized masses. Narrative role of Baindlas is significantly identified through the conduct of rituals and marriage ceremonies intended for Madiga community. Jamidika or javinika is a musical instrument used by Baindlas while narrating the Yellamma story in honour of the deity. The patron-client relation exists not only with the Madigas but also with the people of other castes. For example: Pichakuntlas are the dependent castes for Reddys and Kapus, Runjas and Panasas for Vishvabrahmins, Sadhana shuras and Kunapusalis are for Padmashalis, Mandcchulu and Oggus for Gollas, Gouda Jettus and Yenutis for Goundlas, Gankuntos for Chakalis while Fakkirolu for Kummaris. In the same way, Baindlas are for Madigas.

Nomenclatures of Baindlas vary from one area to another within the state. Bavanis is another term used for them. In the words of Srirama Raju, "the term 'Bavanis' is ascribed to them on the line of the instruments they used to play on. "Their instruments are called Jamidikas. Scholars term the instruments as Bavanikas. Those who play on Bavanikas are known as Bavanis or Baindlas. Bavanika, a musical instrument is also known as 'Pamba.' Through their musical instrument, Baindlas have acquired the name Bavanila by virtue of musical narration about their caste-deity. According to Arudra, the Telugu poet and cine songs writer, 'these Bavanis are known as Pambalas by their instrument called 'Pamba.' Dictionaries have a number of meanings for 'Bavaneelu.' Baindlas are also called 'Bainity' and Asaads by the people of Rayalaseema region. In Andhra, they are called Kommuvaaru while in Telangana, they are known as Bavaneelavaru, Pambalavaru and Jamukulavaaru. Baindlas have acquired their nomenclature through musical instruments they play. The instrument of Baindlas is a symbol of culture. Jamidika is conical in its shape. It is made of wood or bronze. Its rear part is covered with the tender skin of a calf. At the bottom, a string is tightened to a little long wooden piece with a bunch of jingling bells at the end to handle it with the left hand. The shape of Jamidikas is made almost same in all districts of Telangana state.

On the performance by the Baindla artistes, Bonala Prakash writes: "The main signer ties the thick anklets called 'Kejjalu.' He is accompanied by the one Vantha singer holding the sruthimani (sruthi is must for any music the singer's voice should match with its sound) and one Jamidika player. They bow to Goddess Yellamma and narrate her stories. Goddess Yellamma-Renuka Devi is worshipped chiefly by low caste groups across the country. Of course, she is also the main female deity of many families of the upper people. In fact, special ceremonies and worships are conducted during marriages, birth of a child and even at the death of the family members. These performers sing, dance and narrate Yellamma's war against the Kakatiya King Pratap Rudra. Is it not interesting to know that this lady Goddess belongs to a lower caste group challenges and fights against Pratap Rudra? This indicates the role of a woman of lower caste fighting for the injustice done by the rulers and kings. I see this as a strong-willed and empowered lady like Sammakka-Sarakka." (Sphoorthi Theatre STEPARC)

In most cases, Goddess Yellamma-Renuka comes from the lower caste families. Common masses are seen worshipping the deity. Even in urban areas, Yellamma celebrations are conducted during the month of *Ashada* (Equivalent to the month of July).

It was physically observed during field work. Musical players strum the string to produce musical notes in tune with songs. The Baindla *'Jamidika'* carries its myth. Thangirala Venkata Subba Rao is of the view that "while playing spinning top Parshurama is mocked at by his friends as he is fatherless. He questions his mother about his father. She does not answer her son's question and goes into hiding in a trough in the Madiga Street. Parshurama comes in the guise of Pambala playing Jamidika and prays to his mother. She comes out immediately from the trough." (6). It is understood that Jamidika has such power in its musical tone which summons Parashurama's mother from her hiding place.

In the narrative mode the musical practice looks different. In Mahabubnagar district where only two Baindla artistes participate in the act of narration, their narrative looks slightly different from the Baindlas of Khammam and Nalgonda districts. The principal narrator uses the bigger Jamidika while the smaller one is handled by another person. Both Jamidikas produce different musical notes. Bearer of the bigger Jamidika is the master narrator followed by the second one who plays as chorus. A group of performers with a different role for each of them is played in Khammam district. One of them is the master narrator followed by a chorus. All of them are both narrators and performers. The performance starts with the principal performer playing on the Jamidika while the others join with their musical instruments like a small hand-harmonium, one or two pairs of cymbals accompanied by a small drum.

Most of the Baindlas are illiterate. Youngsters of the Baindla community are encouraged to go along with their parents while moving from one place to the other. It is because they have a fear that their children would forget the traditional occupation if they continue further education. Some elders have an apprehension that in pursuit of an occupation other than their caste-based one, the legacy of the artiste community would disappear. They want to protect it in all possible ways.

Elders play on musical instruments while telling stories. The beginners are interested in promoting the caste-based occupation with a concern to protect the Baindla's ancestral occupation. At some other places, the youth, besides pursuing a different profession, evince interest in their caste-based occupation. They make a practice on how to handle the musical instruments such as Jamidika, cymbals and harmonium. They practice telling stories on some occasions and ceremonies like marriages which take place in the families of Madigas. Right from childhood, they get trained in the caste-tradition. In this context, Vijaya Kumar, a journalist of Nampally village in Nalgonda district, who works for the Telugu daily *Andhra Prabha*, said in his interview on 7 January 2017: "The elders of my community enacted dramas which include *Maandatha, Maatah Katha Puranam, Shakthi Kallyanam, Yellamma Pandaga, Manisetti Raya Bhaaram, Bruna Katha*, and won the accolades from the people. We use musical instruments such as cymbals, kinnera and harmonium while narrating stories during festivals."

In Pammy village of Khammam district, the young Baindlas are pursuing higher education and professional courses like Engineering. Besides their higher education, most of the youngsters are fond of ancestral occupation of their elders. C.H. Siva, a Baindla student, doing B. Tech. in computer science, said: "my father is an agricultural labourer. During festivals he narrates stories about the goddess Yellamma through performance in tune with the music being played by other members. Though I am an Engineering student, I am interested in Baindla profession and I often participate in the performance along with my father. I married a bride chosen only from the Baindla community. I strongly believe in the caste-based occupations. I know how to sing and play. We follow only Hindu religion." (Interviewed on 23 January 2017)

When asked about recognition and upliftment of their caste-based occupation, Siva said, "We don't have any kind of recognition nor financial aid either from the Government or from any organization." It can be construed from his words that though the government introduces popular schemes for the benefit of the downtrodden people, it is indifferent to the day-to-day problems of the people and artistes in particular. He further agonizes that the ancestral tradition of his artiste community is on the verge of extinction. One should not forget one's mother, one's own village and ancestral traditions. If it begins to happen in any form, he says, it will be a sign of moral decadence.

In society, one would not distinguish Madigas from Baindlas from socio-economic perspective. But they maintain patron-client relations. On ceremonial occasions, Baindlas act as priests for Madigas. In their ecclesiastical relations, Madigas are bound to honour the priesthood of Baindlas. Priesthood provides them with a special privilege in their mediation with the local gods and goddesses. They conduct marriage ceremonies for Madigas only. They tell stories followed by musical performance in praise of the village deities like Yellamma, Maisamma and Pochamma etc.

Marriage ceremonies of the Baindla community are conducted on lines of folk tradition. Baindlas are not particular about formal exchanges during the marriages. Their families are not particular about the socio-economic status of the other party while negotiating marital alliance. Siva says, "The Baindla elders bring alliances from the community irrespective of its economic status. Marriages are performed as per the Baindla tradition. Even the educated people follow their traditional norms in marriages. Any elder person with knowledge about traditions and customs of his community can act as a priest to conduct ceremonies."

Apart from their caste-based occupation, Baindlas tend to practise foretelling and astrology. They give amulets to the sick people in order to exorcise evil element from their body. Baindla performance is seasonal and it is performed during the summer season. Baindlas practise folk remedy in other times of the year. One Rajam of Rajannapeta village in Siricilla district is an expert in making Jamidikas. He claims that they also do agricultural work apart from foretelling and practising folk remedy. So, they are not fully dependent on their ancestral occupation. This practice is slowly disappearing as it does not interest the Baindla youth.

Baindlas can also be divided into two sub-castes on lines of their patron castes-Mala and Madiga. They are called Madiga Baindla and Mala Baindla. Mala Baindlas do not forge any relation with Madiga Baindlas and vice-versa. Mala Baindlas use only Jamidika, harmonium and dikky whereas Madiga Baindlas do not use any other instrument except dappu. Mala Baindlas are singers while Madiga Baindlas neither sing nor tell stories. In the matrimonial matters, Mala Baindlas intend to establish relations with the people of other castes too which would amount to exogamy. Most of the Baindla people are Christian converts who hardly took to their ancestral occupations. One such person, Kushalaiah, a resident of Anadipeta of Mallepally Mandal in Nalgonda district, shared his experiences in his interview on 28 April 2017: "I do not adopt any of my caste-based occupations. "I do not follow Hindu religion. It is because of this reason I have embraced Christianity. I visit church every Sunday. But I help the Baindla people solve their problems. I act as an adviser to them in many ways." Similarly, P. Krishnaiah, a resident of the same village of Mallepally Mandal in Nalgonda district, claimed in his interview on 28 April 2017: "he is a Baindla priest. He helps conduct rituals and rites, and performs marriage ceremonies. He also encourages participation of people in festivals and organizes public ceremonies."

In the Varna hierarchy, Brahmin class tops the position in Hindu society. It is a priestly class which mediates worship only for the upper caste devotees in temples. Brahmins did not perform pujas and conduct ceremonies for Sudras in the past. The ex-untouchables, known as dalits today, were placed outside the Varna system. Every caste or sub-caste has its dependent castes. Dependent castes are mostly the artistes in their respective fields. Similarly, the Baindlas are dependent castes for Madigas. Through their artistic performances during marriage ceremonies and other rituals, Baindlas command respect as priests from their patrons. Thus, they have got priestly place by virtue of their caste-based occupation.

Baindlas are not only artistes but also act as priests for Madigas. In social sub-caste hierarchy, Madigas consider Baindlas as inferior to them. Brahmins were not willing to perform pujas for any dalit in the past. Now the situation is different in both rural and urban areas. It is because priesthood is commodified and commercialized where priestly services are sold for money regardless of one's caste. Rich dalits living in cosmopolitan environment engage Brahmin priests to conduct ceremonies and worships during marriages and other rituals. The urban Brahmin pundits would not mind performing pujas for dalits as they get handsome payment. Baindlas are sporadically seen conducting ceremonies for dalits and they are playing the role of Brahmins for their Madiga patrons in villages. Inter-dining exists between Madigas and Baindlas. This practice is discernible especially during marriages and other ceremonies. They also sing songs eulogizing the local deities. They eke out their living through the caste-based occupation.

Though bigamy is legally unacceptable, it is strongly practised by the dependent castes. This takes place with the consent of elders of the Baindla community. Baindla men prefer bigamy for occupational reasons. When they take a trip for their performance in different villages, they want their first wives to go along with them to help in performance while the second wife would stay home to take care of the children and the livestock. Their marital relations are endogamous. They don't go for inter-caste marriages. They prefer endogamous marriages. If any member of their caste prefers inter-varna, he/she can be excommunicated from the community. This appears to be a rigid norm in their community. Thus, they strictly follow the endogamous rule. However, in the changing society, the educated youth enjoy freedom in choosing their partners for marriage in spite of the norms prescribed by their community.

Apart from the already existing records about the Baindla community, a field-based study was conducted to explore their current socio-cultural status. Generally, two Baindla artistes are involved in the narrative performance. They use their musical instruments in performance. One of them acts as the main narrator and the other keeps repeating the sequence of narration. The bigger Jamidika is handled by the main narrator while the smaller one by the second person. No other people are part of their singing. Often, they narrate the *Yellamma Katha* or Yellamma story eulogizing the birth of Yellamma goddess. They narrate the story in tune with the Jamidika. The two Jamidikas produce different musical notes.

Polepally, a village, is located about 125 kms away from Hyderabad and 50 kms from Mahabubnagar district headquarters. Only one Baindla family is spotted in the entire village. Male narrators of the family members conduct marriage ceremonies and other rituals for Madigas. Besides occasional narrative performances, they often do the labour work in agricultural fields. Their endogamous position does not permit them to exercise priesthood for non-dalit families. No marital relations are allowed between Baindlas and Madigas. Baindlas dine with Madigas during celebrations while the Madigas do not share with Baindlas in other times. However, Baindlas act as priests for Madigas as a convention. Thus, they are associated with Madiga community. There is no practice of untouchability between these sub-castes while Madigas practice it with Dakkalis. With the change of caste-based occupations, either Madigas or Dakkalis are not identified by their social category until and unless they claim that they belong to a certain category in society. The young generation does not want to claim caste privileges. Rajennapeta is a village in Siricilla district about 250 kms away from Hyderabad. The village has only one Baindla family consisting of 3 members. Their performance is similar to that of the Mahabubnagar Baindlas. The male member of the family mobilizes other Baindla artistes for the programme. They find opportunities seasonally to conduct their performances. In the harvest season, they do labour along with other communities in the village.

Pammy, a village in Mudigonda Mandal of Khammam district, is about 270 kms away from Hyderabad. The village has 10 Baindla families while Nelakondaipally has four families only. In two villages, only 8 artistes are active with their hereditary occupation. The band of performers comprises five artistes. One of them acts as a principal performer who dances in tune with ankle bells. Other members keep playing the musical instruments according to the line of narration. Despite these artistic performances, they earn a little for their survival. For them, art is not for art's sake but for the sake of their livelihood. Their economic conditions are precarious. They also do physical labour in the absence of the village celebrations. Most of the Baindla families depend on the *Asara* pensions extended by the State Government.

In various Mandals in Nalgonda district, eighteen Baindla families are found. The district has a total of twenty-four active artistes. They conduct marriage ceremonies and rituals only for Madigas. Most of the youth are the converted Christians. The young generation is interested in modern life because of religious conversion. They are averse to the traditional practices in Hinduism. They reject superstitious beliefs. They prefer other professions to their ancestral occupation. Converted Christians financially help those who have not converted to Christianity. The four districts mentioned above have sparse Baindla population with 32 families in all, which have been located in the interior villages. Only one family in Polepalli village of Mahabubnagar district is figured out while Siricilla too has only one Baindla family.

Some villages in Khammam and Nalgonda districts are highly populated with these communities when compared to other districts. The actual Baindla population appears to have been reduced due to its conversion to Christianity. The original Baindla population is dismal. The second and third generation youth hardly prefer the hereditary occupation and they are left with no other option but to do labour work along with the people of the other communities. It is because they hardly receive patronage from their patron communities for artistic performance. With support and encouragement extended by the elders of their community, some young people from the same family continue to evince interest in their caste-based occupation.

It is understood that the Baindla occupation and its traditional sheen remain on the verge of extinction due to lack of patronage from the patron classes and public as well. The youth of the new generation have started to explore fresh avenues to replace the hereditary occupation for their livelihood. The Baindla occupation is sparsely practised; agricultural labour majorly provides them sustenance. At some places, aged Baindlas are still interested in hereditary occupations. But they are physically unable to promote this occupation. Their younger generation is not interested in the continuation of the ancestral caste-based occupation given the modern changes in professionalism. The youth are inclined to adopt different professions which have no caste stigma. This can be viewed as a changing socio-cultural scenario of the community.

Chindus as Folk Performing Artistes

Chindus constitute a dependent caste for Madigas. 'Chindu' is a Telugu word which is a synonym for *Natyam, Nritam* and *Natakam* (dance and drama). 'Chindu' is the other name for performing art. It would also mean 'a vibrant step' which is a uniquely patterned expression that looks like a dance. It would also mean 'jump.' The performance of the Chindus is interspersed with leaps and jumps. One view is that a section of people within the Madiga community have taken to dancing as profession. They are called Chindu Madigas; 'Cindu' means a dance step. Another view is that the word 'Cindu' is derived from 'Sindu' that means ocean. Chindu dancers and movements of their steps look like the waves of the ocean. According to Gaddam Rammohan Rao who explored the origin of Chindus, there is a mention of Chindus even in ancient literature.

There was no earth, no water, no light, no wind, no sky, and no Brahma, no Vishnu and Maheshwara. There were also no stars. There were no Sun and Moon either. There was nothing, nihility all over, pitch darkness. At that time, 'Om' was the only sound that existed. Masuk originated out of 'Onkara' and rain originated out of masku, rain fell into the sea. A mass of rain created numerous water beds. A bubble originated out of water beds. A whirl was formed out of the bubble. A conch emerged and from the conch Primordial Jambavantha was born. While introducing himself, Primordial Jambava dances by singing several kinds of songs. That dance is called 'Chindu.' We understand that the origin of 'Chindu' is as old as the birth of Jambavantha.

Mohan Rao, in his book *Chindula Yellamma*, builds a very interesting argument that "the study of legends helped the scientists like Darwin in their research. He says that the birth of Jambavantha and Darwin's theory of evolution share similarities. According to Darwin's theory of evolution, the entire universe was covered with water. A moss came out later. It had water creatures like fishes, frogs. Then the monkeys came. There was an evolution of human beings from the monkey family. The evolution of human being is akin to the birth of Jambava. *Jambapurana* is the source of all scientific aspects in the world." (96)

Thus, it has acquired the name of Chindu Bhagavatham. We have historical sources on this performing art. Chindus are those who perform *yakshaganas.* Madigas were/are treated as one of the outcastes living outside the Varna system. They are also called *Panchama Varna* and hence untouchables. Their principal occupation is involved in the disposal of dead carcasses. They pursue skinning and tanning to get leather for shoe-making.

Apart from already existing records about the Baindla community, a field-based study was conducted mandal-wise to explore its current socio-cultural status. Several facts came to light. Chindus live majorly in five districts of Telangana: Siddipet, Karimnagar, Nalgonda and Warangal. Tukkapuram village in Togutta Mandal of Siddipet district has only one Chindu family comprising three members. K. Sanjeev of the Chindu family is a dedicated artiste who hails from another district and joins the Chindu Mela. Besides this, he also involves himself in agricultural labour during harvest season.

Desaipalle is a village in Siricilla district which has only three Baindla families. There are three artistes, one from each family. They visit other villages to mobilize their fellow artistes. On some specific occasions, they do performances and most of the time in a year they also do agricultural labour because their caste-based artistic performance does not earn much. They cannot feed their families with this meagre earning. However, they want to continue this hereditary occupation not for the sake of money but for the sake of art and its heritage. The embedded sense is that they are poised to enliven the Chindu art.

Pochampally village in Gurrampudu Mandal, Dharveshpuram in Kalagallu Mandal, Nermettu village in Chanduru Mandal, Nakkalapally village in Narketpall Mandal, Gudipaka village in Mallepally Mandal and Nampally village in Nalgonda district have high concentration of Chindu population. About 68 Chindu families are located in all villages of the district. Of these families, 42 artistes are active in their performance. In response to the invitation from Madiga community, they visit Madiga villages and give performances during festive seasons. The participant performers are paid *Kattadi* or honorarium by Madiga community. They do not receive patronage from Madigas. Their patronage is not same all the time. So Chindu performers do not take up performances throughout the year. They find it difficult to earn enough to feed their families. That is why the Chindu youth do labour work along with the people of other communities.

Nermettu village in Chandur Mandal of Nalgonda district has 16 Chindu families. Of these sixteen families, 3 families are associated with shoe-making. It is the rarest of the rare case that some Chindus who have not shown interest in the hereditary occupation have switched to truck driving and shoemaking. On enquiry about their caste-based occupation they say that their elders who were the performing artistes did not encourage them much in that direction. Their unwillingness is another reason for discontinuity of their performance. They claim that they are able to make at least one pair of designed shoes in a day. They do this occupation much better than their patron class. They make shoes which they fondly call *Kanpur* foot-wear. It has become popular in the surrounding areas. They are proud of shoe-making. They claim that they made a pair of *Kanpur* foot-wear for Late Rajasekhar Reddy, the former Chief Minister of undivided Andhra Pradesh. They were handsomely paid. They narrated this experience with pride.

Besides shoe-making, Chindus also go for vegetable-selling in the market. They eke out their livelihood through other means too because their performance is not a yearlong activity. Public response is poor in rainy season. Moreover, the traditional performance is not watched by the youth. They prefer watching films and other programmes on mobiles. Traditional performances have lost their sheen due to the onslaught of development of technology. Like theatrical performances Chindu performance has lost its ancestral glory for lack of patronage from the Madigas and the general public. Gadda village of Nalgonda District presents this miserable scenario.

As per the myth, Madigas are destined to do menial and polluting jobs like skinning dead animals in villages. The Madiga caste myth enumerates eighteen *yugas* (ages) unlike the classical version of four *yugas.* Jambavamuni is the direct ancestor of Madigas. He was said to have been born in the *Adbhuta Yuga*, the fourth of the eighteen Yugas. In the *Bhinnaja Yuga,* the ninth Yuga, Parabrahma, the creator, was keen to perform the marriage of Trimurtis. On this occasion, Parabrahma created Pancha Brahmas to produce the material required for the wedlock. Pancha Brahmas are assigned the work of melting the mountains of gold, silver and bronze for making ornaments, vessels etc.

Manu Brahma, the eldest of the Pancha Brahmas, approached Jambavamuni as per the directions of Parabrahma for a leather bagpipe to melt the mountains of gold, silver and bronze. Jambavamuni was in dilemma on how to procure leather without killing an animal. Jambavamuni was advised to create Yugamuni from his right rib. Acting on Parbrahma's advice, Jambavamuni killed Yugamuni and made a leather pipe from his skin. While dying, Yugamuni cursed Jambavamuni to become an outcaste. Jambavamuni pleaded that he was innocent and was forced to kill him as a sacred duty. Then Yugamuni reduced his capital punishment to a curse which was to be valid for five thousand years. The validity of the curse affected the posterity of Jambavamuni who became outcastes.

Panchbrahmas made all the required paraphernalia out of metals by using leather pipe as furnace to melt mountains. The marriage of Siva and Parvati was performed with pomp and glory. Vana Vihara Parthi got hurt in her thigh. She removed a bit of her thigh flesh and threw it on cow dung. Chennaiah was born out of it. Parvati created a divine cow namely '*Jamili Kamadhenu* or Jamili gangi govu.' The milk of the cow was very tasty and Chennaiah thought that the flesh of the cow might be tastier than the milk. On hearing this news, Kamadhenu committed suicide in front of the hermitage of Siva. The devatas (gods) then tried to remove the carcass but failed. Then they asked Chennaiah to go to 'Jambalapuri Patnam' to call Jambavamuni for his advice. Chennaiah addressed Jambavamuni as "O tata Maha digira instead of calling Madigira because of *Visha Vaakku* (evil spirit) in his tongue. That is how Madiga came into vogue because of Chennaiah's tongue twister." (115)

Besides this profession, Madigas do menial jobs concerning nature purity and pollution. They are also treated as untouchables like Chindus. They were/are victims of social injustice. In fact, they are not associated with the skin based occupation. They eke out their livelihood from the Madiga community through their artistic performances for which some honorarium is paid. In the past, they would go from one village to another with their artistic performance and would collect *Thyagam* (traditional honorarium paid by the patrons). They are stationary in their habitations now. But they visit other villages where they require giving performance and come back to their village. Gaddam Sammaiah claims: 'Performing Chindu troupes keep a picture of Goddess Yellamma before them and move around the villages to collect whatever the villagers give, be it clothes or food. Generally, they avoid performances in monsoon season. When not performing, they work as farm labour or do fishing and rope making.' (96)

To promote the welfare schemes of the government and other programmes which include environmental protections, sanitation, family planning, literacy, awareness of TB, AIDS, the services of Chindus are used. These messages are incorporated in their *Yakshaganas* for entertainment. In Sammayya's words, "We are able to survive because of the remuneration government gives us for this" (*The Hindu,* Friday Review 96). Thus, Government comes to their rescue by providing funds for costumes and accessories. But such assistance may not be same to all the performing Chindu artistes of the state. It is because the dominant group within the community ultimately enjoys the benefits.

Chindus are caste-children of Madigas who play a parental role in social relations. "Within the Madiga community, a sect considered itself as 'Pedda Madiga' (Head Madiga) and another sect that lives on begging and performing *yakshaganas* is called 'Chinna Madigas' or Deputy Madiga" (265). In fact, these Chindu Bhagavatas were not permitted to perform beyond their own community. Chindus, as dependent caste, are in the service of Madigas who would offer paddy, clothes and cattle in return for their artistic performances. Honorarium paid to the Chindus is called by different names like Katnam, Thyagam, Mera, Mirasi, Vanthana and Vathanu: all these terms mean the same. An annual honorarium is paid to dependent castes as a tradition for their performances which eulogize the greatness of the patron culture and its place in society. Each Chindu family chooses a few Madiga households from the respective villages earmarked for their patronage. In this, Chindus visit each Madiga village in a year with a sojourn which may last more than a week and they collect their honorarium for performing *Yakshagana* and *Bagotham.* The entire expenditure is borne by Chindus. After completing their performance, they move to another village. Thus, they seek patronage from the Madiga families to meet their expenditure related to performances.

Chindus are one of the sub-castes within the dalit community.

Chindus as discussed in the previous chapter come under the dependent caste associated with Madigas. They give artistic performances from *Yakshagana* and *Bhagavatham* for which Madigas pay money. They play musical steps during their performance. Chindu means a musical step. Thus, they are known as Chindus by virtue of their rhythmic steps. They are also known as Chindu artistes or Chindu Madigas. The *Yakshagana* that they perform is called Chindu *Bagotham* or Chindu *Bhagavatham*. Krishnaiah Gaddam quotes from *Chindula Yellamma*. In their performance, they create aesthetic pleasure from the stories taken from the *Bhagavatham*. Krishnaiah says:

> With his son, Jambavantha goes to the world of gods. All the gods find *Yakshagana* of Yakshas in trance. Knowing Jambava's coming, Yaksha salutes and addresses him as Munidra, "Your visit is a happy one and you are the one who has offered *bhikṡha* or alms to our Yakshaganas. You received applause from one and all for your Sindhu dance. I wish to watch Sindhu dance once. Please don't say 'no.'" Jambavanth blesses his son Jimahamuni as he is unable to dance due to the mountain being stuck in his calf. Yakshas and gods who were stunned with singing and dancing skills give big claps. Then Yaksha appreciates the singing and dancing skill of Jinmhamuni and blesses him saying that 'may you become famous on earth in the art of Chindu Yakshaganas'. (My trans. 13)

Generally, Chindus perform Yakshaganas during daytime. They create feast to the eyes of the public through their marvelous performances from the legends, though most of them are illiterate. Thus, the performers are called *pagativeshagallu* or matinée idols. The reason for their performance during the day is attributed to poverty. They cannot afford to buy oil for night lamps or petromaxes. Chindu population is mostly concentrated in several districts of the Telangana state. Chindu Bhagavata which is a living art has been performed for centuries. Characters perform their respective roles by singing.

The band of *Bhagavata* performers are known as '*Bhagavatham Mela*.' Each Chindu family becomes a band of *bhagavata* performers. They themselves form *Melas* or troupes. Each Mela comprises 12 to 30 artistes. Each of them plays either a musical instrument or performs a prescribed role. They do not allow others from outside to join their *Mela*. All these artistes share the villages among them. Performers of one village do not transgress into the other. They also live on the dalit street and accept groceries for cooking offered by the dalits. They give two or three performances first free of honorarium. They charge further performances. Most of the stories narrated by them are derived from *Bhagavatham.* Gaddam Sammayya who leads the performing troupes claims that though Chindus trace their origin to Jamba Mahamuni, and believe that their clan is the most ancient one. Sammaiah further says that due to this reason most of their dramas open with *Jambapurana*. In the opening *pallavi* (prelude), he says:

> *'Ekkuvani Mari Palukabokumura, Ekkuvevvaru mari TelisiPalukumura* (95-96)
> (Don't speak of being high, speak knowing who is higher).

Several Chindus are scholars in Sanskrit, Prakrit and Telugu. Some of them can speak Urdu also and some other people have written in Sanskrit. It is Chindus who have preserved *Jambapurana* and the ideas of household remedies through *taalpatras* (palm leaves; palm leaf manuscripts were a primitive method of recording ancient knowledge on such leaves).

Apart from performing different roles in formal costumes, they also sing openly on contemporary social problems related to rural life. Gurumurthy, a Chindu youth of Pammy village in Nampally mandal of Nalgonda district, was interviewed on 8 January 2017. He sang a song in Telugu in a public meeting. The song was recorded and later translated into English for use in research. It depicted the condition of the village when all the people have migrated to towns and cities. The village wears a deserted look without potters, goldsmiths, blacksmiths, farmers and other craftsmen of productive classes and castes.

Village Migrated

Desolation is visible all over
Rural games stop
Song turns mute
Village wears a deserted look
A sight of collapsed furnace
Satyanna, the desolate potter
No bangs of wash reverberate
Brahmchari, the carpenter
Appears to be a stranger
Caste-based callings are disarrayed
Starvation deaths are escalated
No crops, no greenery
Bird chirping goes mute
Nowhere are seen ears of tender corn
No cultivated lands are in sight
No heaps of grain are around
No offerings are made to the deity
He wanders in utter distress
It is true, crowbars turn blunt
No hammer bangs are heard
Rock terrains turn silent
He moves from place to place
Village is not a village as before
Loom turns mute in weaver's house
Colour dying wheels too stop
No elegant sarees are in sight
Saranna is caught in trouble
Herd of sheep falls sick
Mute lives fly into the air
There is no timely medicine
Middle men rob the whole
What happens to a shepherd?

He becomes a migrated bird
No glitter in goldsmith's house
Fire pot mocks at him
Whole life turned insipid
Houses wail with squealing cry
He is lost in the stream.

The song depicts the desolate village. Most of the villagers have migrated to urban areas. Industrialization occupies the place, which marginalizes the caste-based occupations. Village craftsmen have lost their livelihood. No crops are raised in the fields nor there is greenery sprawled all over for want of rains. There would be chirping birds swaying on the tender ears of corn across the fields and there are no such sights now. No grain heaps are seen and no offerings are made to the deities. Fertile lands have turned into waste lands and the farm wells which amply irrigated are now in dilapidated condition. Machines are pressed into breaking the boulders; nothing is spared to the stone-cutters whose cutting tools have turned blunt and rhyming sound turned mute pushing the stone cutters into migration. The song also touches upon the life of shepherds whose herd of goats and sheep become prone to various diseases. The trading broker of the sheep loots the whole. The shepherd leaves the village like a migrated bird. The goldsmith's house would glitter with gold, now it is with no glory as his fire-pot mocks at him. The desolated houses wail with squealing cry. The goldsmith is drowned in the stream, perhaps he could be washed away in the current of gushing water.

The song is a portrayal of the desolate life of the villagers who have missed cultivation for want of rains. This also affects the caste-based occupations which disappear leaving the occupants helpless, who choose to migrate to towns and cities for their livelihood. The song also draws on apathy of the rulers who never care for the rural welfare. This indicates failure of the rulers in the creation of the rural employment in order to check the mass migration. Chindu songs have evolved from the pathetic condition that the common people confronted with.

Folk legends speak about the birth and fury of Yellamma, the local goddess. The emergence of Yellamma is a marvelous episode both in the *Gouda Purana* and the *Jambapurana.* According to *Gosangipurana*, Adishakti emerges and dies of the wild effect of Siva's third eye. Her burnt ash is collected and separated into four parts. Out of each part, Sarasvati, Parvati, Laxmi and Yellamma are born respectively. During the formation of the earth, Yellamma, with her furious emotions, creates havoc. Jambavantha, the great grandfather of the Madigas, wears a nicker laced with jingling bells and also wears ankle bells around his ankles. He wields a curved sword. His eyes become red. He appears with combed moustaches amidst percussions. He is ready to propitiate the furious Yellamma. Jambavamuni or Jambavantha is endowed with such power which can propitiate the irate gods and goddesses. Chindus perform the *Gosangipurana.* They narrate *Jambapurana* through singing. *Jambapurana* is performed through the Yakshagana while *pattam katha* or reading maps comprise various pictures drawn by Dakkalis. It was performed as proclaimed by the Madiga guru" (46). Chindus narrate the *Bhagavata* and the *Ramayana*, and also the stories of *Ankamma* along with *Jambapurana.* They are associated with the performing art. They choose to perform the *puranas* in the heart of the village to attract all castes which constitute the audience for their performance.

Vernacular literatures discuss the myths of local goddesses like Yellamma who is popularly known as Chindu Yellamma. Her autobiography mirrors her culture. Chindus never step into the village without the permission of Madigas. It is a traditionally embedded caste norm. In preference, they perform from the point of Madigas and later for others. As a tradition, first they offer prayers to the trough (a huge vessel in which hides are soaked in lime), and then begin their performance. They make an agreement with Madigas on their honorarium. The agreement is made for the fixed payment. They perform a play called *Chindu Bhagotham* marking anniversaries in the village.

Village elders visit the Madiga Street with a goat for sacrifice. The chief of the village touches the Madiga trough with reverence after spreading a cloth with turmeric on it. He breaks the coconut. They believe that goddess Yellamma resides in the trough, a big oval-shaped earthen pot which is used for tanning. A Chindu woman plays Yellamma who goes dancing to the tune of the drum-beating. She is carried to the *acupacchani pandiri* or green pandal. She wields a sword in one hand and a few shoots of neem leaves in the other hand.

Chindu Yellamma dances in rhythmic steps displaying her ferocity. When she tumbles down, the spirit goes off from her. The woman is woken up amidst songs. After she comes back to her senses, the goat is revolved around her. Again, she goes into the possession of the goddess. A Chindu magician asks the villagers whether goat should be sacrificed. He executes it with the consent of all the people. He fiercely bites the goat. Thus, they propitiate the goddess by breaking coconut or cutting off lemons. With this ritual, the goddess cools down. Potharaju, who lashes whips on the individuals of the community, showers blessings on the houses of his community people while walking down to the temple. He lifts the head of the goat in public display to make sure that the goat is sacrificed.

Dakkalis as Untouchables among Dalits

Social movements launched by Dr. Saheb Ambedkar for emancipation of the people of his community brought social awareness. The historical fact cannot be denied. Dalits began to protect their self-respect in all spheres of their activities. The most oppressed people lying at the bottom of society are yet to be brought to the limelight. Ambedkar's struggles have emancipated many socially oppressed groups; but the fruits of his struggles have not reached out to many people. It is undeniable fact that the main castes within the community, which are on the forefront, have benefitted from reservation more than their sub-castes and dependent castes. Dependent castes are still struggling for survival and are at the mercy of their patron castes/classes. They are left neglected and denied equal share of reservation benefits. Madiga Dandora Movement brought this fact to limelight. Artistic performance of the dependent castes was not so promising. Not much literature is produced about the life and culture of dependent castes. Dalit elitist writers consider a few of the principal castes in their discourse in order to represent the entire dalit community.

The origin of the kinnera is still unclear. Swathi, quoting Jayadhir Thirumala Rao, says: "There is no plausible explanation for how the kinnera came to be part of the Dakkali group while losing its relevance where it had originated. Groups from the Chenchu tribe might have been influenced by the 'Sramanaka' culture of Buddhism, and left their tribal life to be part of the caste hierarchy" (n.p.).

According to a gory anecdote, a Chenchu woman was cutting vegetables and was listening to the mellifluous notes cascading from her husband's kinnera. Lost in the music, she cut up her infant too. The entire tribe was horrified and banned the instrument from the hills. Basically, the instrument is traced to the tribal groups. Swathi argues that it is their cultural legacy. This might have shifted to the hands of the Dakkali community at a later stage.

As discussed earlier, Dakkalis/Dakkalas like Baindlas and Chindus constitute lesser population and depend upon the Madiga community. Unlike other dependent castes, they were treated as untouchables. Even Madigas including Chindus and Baindlas did not allow them to mingle with them. Thus, they remained untouchables among untouchables. In fact, Madigas are on the top next to Malas in sub-caste hierarchy. Contemporary emancipatory struggles are yet to be carried out by dalits to curb the dominance of sub-caste hierarchy within the community. The pyramid of caste structure is deep-rooted in Indian culture and the same is duplicated among lower castes too. This discussion focuses on the narrative art of Dakkalis, socio-cultural relations with their patron community and relevance of *Jambapurana*.

The word 'Dakkali' is derived from 'Dakka' which means 'vertebral column.' Dakkalis are born from the vertebral column of the Madigas. *Jambapurana* narrates a myth that Jambhava, the primordial man of the Madiga community, is also known as Jambavamuni, Jambavantha, Jambavanthu, Jambhavudu. He killed his son and made various instruments with the parts of his body and gave them to a Vishwakarma or Goldsmith. Jambava brought his son back to life from his unused backbone. But Jambava disallowed the boy to be associated with caste. The boy became a Dakkali/Dakkala.

There is another story about Dakkali caste. For want of necessary tools, goldsmith was unable to make a gold locket or marriage token/badge for Shiva's wedding. Jambava came to know the inconvenience of goddesses, and ensured required tools like bellows, fire-pot, hammer, etc. Vishwa Brahma prepared the chain and sent it. To her utter surprise, Parvati comes to know that Jambava sacrificed his younger son, Jagamuni, and converted all the parts of his body into the required tools. Parvati was very firm that her marriage should take place only after Jagamuni comes to life. Vishwabrahma recreates Jagamuni out of his thoracic. Thus, Dakkalis are the offspring of Jagamuni. But Jambamuni rejects the deeds of Vishwabrahma. He requests him to serve Madigas who are offspring of his eldest son, Jagamuni. Since then, Dakkalis became mendicants and served as folk doctors for Madigas. As Thurston says, Jagamuni is told that he must live as a beggar attached to the Madiga community. He is called Dakkala because he is brought to life from a vertebral column-*dakka/dokka* (104). Dakkalis make a living by narrating stories and glorifying the hereditary cultural legacy of Madigas. In fact, they were nomadic people. With the passage of time, Dakkali youth changed hereditary occupation and took to different professions for survival. They moved from one village to another and stayed there for some days begging food from the houses of Madigas who were traditionally bound to offer them money, food and other gifts. They sang folk songs and narrated the Madiga cultural history. They used a musical instrument called kinnera which is "a magnificent string instrument with a bamboo neck, dried and hollowed gourds as resonators, strings made of human hair or animal nerves (replaced now with metal), and pangolin scales for frets" (*The Hindu*).

Generally, only a single person is involved in singing the exploits of the local legends. The act of oral performance or singing does not need any particular open place for a stage. Each person narrates on his/ her own. While singing they would strum the different steps of Kinnera. A group of Madiga villagers sit as audience around the narrator. It is a solo performance which would last one hour or less. Jayadheer Thirumala Rao says: "The castes riddled with a feeling of inferiority stood and continued to stand as repositories of culture. Civil society begins to recognize it. The culture that comes out of it is unlimited. 'It is a kind of awareness given to contemporary dalit social movements" (46).

The views expressed by Thirumala Rao are true. It is because Dakkalis are made to feel inferior to other castes. Encouragement of dependence will promote subordination. It is true of Dakkalis. The culture of these communities is not promoted by the government or by the patron class. They are still riddled with inferiority complex because of imposed low social position. Puranas are repositories of culture. In that *Jambapurana* is a treasury of the Madiga community which Dakkalis eulogize through the narration. The educated elitists even among the patron castes do not evince interest to promote it through the discourse. The economically flourishing Madigas never attempt to talk about it as they feel that the cultural subject of this kind would subordinate their position. But the promoters of Madiga community discovered their cultural roots in *Jambapurana* through the narrations of the Dakkali artistes and Nulaka Chandayya, the guru of Madigas. "*Jambapurana* delineates the Madiga culture. Chindus perform *Jambapurana* through Yakshagana while Madiga Mastis perform it through a musical narration; Baindlas give folk performance while Dakkalis narrate it as *Pattam Katha*, the street play while Nulaka Chandayyas proclaim it in a *purana* form" (46).

Dakkalis narrate and give their performance with an inspiration from the *Jambapurana*. This ancient text foregrounds Madiga culture and way of life. Madigas are enlightened through Dakkali narration. *Jambapurana* counters the ashtadasa puranas and thus stands parallel to them. In the words of Rao and Prabhakar: "Dakkali performers have been preserving their *Jambpurana* and continuing it as a parallel purana by giving performances, without association with the ashtadasa puranas and the other upa-puranas. This is the highest form of 'Cultural Revolution'. And this is also their cultural achievement" (n.p.).

Besides their artistic performance, Dakkalis also practise folk remedy with herbs. They believe in traditional cure which gives no side effects. They also feel that folk remedy is safe though it takes a longer time for cure. To promote the herbal treatment, they do not go to any allopathic or homeopathic doctor for treatment. Herbal knowledge folk remedy is inherited from their ancestors.

It is also the 'Kulapurana' of Madigas. It says: "There is no fixed text or single narrative. Its multiple narratives are performed by Madiga dependent communities like Dakkali, Chindu, Baindla, Nulaka Chandayya, and others. *Jambapurana* is the ancient purana of Madigas. "*Jambapurana* serves as a model even for other Kulapuranas" (Nanuma n.p.).

There are puranas like Saiva, Vaishnava and Virasaiva, blended with Shaktheya philosophy and they continue to incorporate some parts of the main puranas into their respective *Kulapuranas*. "It is only the Dakkali *Jambapurana* that clearly exposes the shallowness of the dominant puranas. This purana becomes the centre of the dialogue initiated between the Brahmin and Jambavamuni in such a way that it allows Jambava to challenge Brahminical narrative assertion of caste hegemony."

Simon Charsely says, "Jambava ridicules Brahminical ideas of proper descent and many radical separations are visible between the Brahmin and the Madiga".

> Don't feel that you are superior and Madigas are inferior
> Oh fool! Do you know who was superior
> And who was inferior in the past?
> Oh Brahmin, you are the son of the donkey Brahmins are the slaves of other castes
> To whom was Vyasa born?
> Was he born to the Madigas or to the Kings? (135)

The Madiga challenges the so-called superior Brahmin. He tries to enlighten the Brahmin about the past relating to the binary of inferiority and superiority. He reveals the stunning facts of the Brahmin saying that they were the sons of donkeys and slaves of other castes, the facts of which Brahmins should be aware. Madiga further refers to the Maharishi Vyasa and his birth. The Brahmin became speechless with Madiga's stunning counter argument. He tries to establish the true identity of Madiga. In the words of Jayadheer Thirumala Rao: "There is an argument between Jambava and Brahmin. It is a direct protest, opposition and on the caste hegemony. Jambava satirizes the superiority complex of the Brahmin. There is a logic but emotional and sometimes it takes a form of humiliation. In Dakkali Jambapurana, a war is waged against the upper caste domination but it can be declared in a mild way that "It is more of a comic and humorous than logic" (xix).

The Dakkali culture is discussed in regional/vernacular literature. Yendluri Sudhakar, a dalit poet, is the first to bring Dakkali caste into his poem titled *Pilla* (Lass). Gunde Dappu Kanakaiah reflects it in his *Dakkali Yetha* (Agony of Dakkalis). *Jambapurana* has an excellent portrayal of Jambavantha. We do not see any sculptured images of such historical personalities are characteristics of *pattams.* Pictures are visible in them drawn by the folk artists. There is a five and a half-foot statue of Jambavamuni in Sulluripeta in Nelluru district of Andhra Pradesh. The statue is regularly worshipped. This area remains a testimony to a battlefield of Krishna-Jambavamuni. Yendluri Sudhakar's *Mallemoggala Godugu* portrays Jambavamuni but it does not elaborate much on the Dakkali caste. Jupakasubadra's *Maanyam* (The Gifted Land), a short story, depicts the Dakkali culture. For Dakkalis, traditional begging is a hereditary occupation. They do not beg from any other community except the Madiga community. Dakkalis have a hereditary right to demand the Madigas to feed them. The Telugu vernacular literature carries a legacy of Dakkali culture and their relationship with the patron community.

The habitations of Dakkalis are narrow in their construction. They erect makeshift huts structured in long-curved reeds/sticks covered with water-proof sheets in low heights. They are so narrow and short that one can only sit in the huts but cannot stand in them. All their huts are narrowly built with a half oval shaped front opening. The huts are not enough ventilated. They live on the fringes of *Madiga wada* (Madiga ghettos). Their locations are unhygienic with weeds growing in the surroundings. The moonlight is the natural light for them. Most of the time, they sleep in the open in front of their huts. They use small kerosene lamps or lanterns at night. They raise fire into flames which provides them with faint light that flickers during their dining at nights. In rainy seasons, they take night meals in the evening itself. In case of heavy rains and winds, they move into abandoned houses. There is no proper protection for their domestic animals. However, they have natural strength to withstand natural calamities.

Dakkali women are the skilled weavers of mats and baskets. They take their product into the market for sale. Thus, they earn some subsidiary income to meet their sundry expenses. This apart, they also rear domestic animals such as goats and hens which move around their habitations. Besides their hereditary occupation, they also go for hunting into nearby woodlands. It is construed that their traditional occupation does not sufficiently feed them. So, they depend upon the other means to eke out their living. Untouchability is a byproduct of caste system which is a hierarchal phenomenon in Hindu society. It is practised by the upper castes against the lower castes and the same practice is replicated by the lower castes against the lowest of the low. This is a real tragedy in the caste world. There are innumerable instances to bring in to justify this fact. In Telugu states, Mala is the principal caste among other lower castes. Next to this comes the Madiga in the hierarchy. In caste gradation, they themselves claim as a higher category among the Dalits. Most of Malas in villages still practise untouchability against Madigas and other sub-castes. This is an open practice in the rural milieu while in urban areas, it is not so open but it is perceived through one's attitude towards Madiga community. Madigas view this as prejudiced and discriminatory within the community. They are of the view that their sub-caste brethren are not bothered about physical touch like many other upper castes but they attempt to hegemonize the available physical resources for their use at maximum level at the cost of the other sub-castes. This situation caused a sort of imbalance and created socio-economic disparity within the community.

Though Madigas are next to Malas in hierarchy, Madigas too play an upper caste role against Dakkalis. Madigas don't allow Dakkalis to come into their houses. There was a rigid practice of untouchability between Madigas and Dakkalis in the past. Surprisingly, Dakkalis also claim an upper caste position in their relation with *Mustis and Mondis* and treat them as inferior. Dakkali Ramulu of Odicharla village in Mahabubnagar district is a strong case in point, who goes to the Madiga families singing songs and narrating stories without kinnera, the traditional musical instrument. In his interview on 5 March 2017, he speaks about his relation with Madigas: "I am not allowed into the Madiga families. So, I sit in front of their houses or in the front yards. I still cling to my hereditary occupation of begging food and money from the Madiga patrons. I eke out my livelihood by hunting birds and other small animals, and sell them for money. I live in a small makeshift hut with my family."

A Dakkali young man turned to rickshaw-pulling as he could not afford to feed the family through his hereditary occupation. This can be cited as one of the reasons why he gave up the caste-based ancestral occupation. The other reason for choosing this work can be attributed to his unwillingness to pursue his ancestral occupation as it is linked to the sub-caste/dependent caste category, which is considered a social stigma in society. Dakkali young men don't want to be branded as untouchables through their hereditary occupation. In fact, they desire for a change in their lifestyle. Thus, they tend to escape the stigma of untouchability and caste discrimination by abjuring their hereditary occupation.

In rural Telangana, most of the Dakkalis depend upon

Madigas but not on the other castes. They say that their cultural tradition doesn't permit them to do so. They believe in Madiga patronage, a traditional contribution. In the past too, they were not allowed to enter the courtyards of Madigas. Now they begin to reside in the close proximity of Madiga families. They entertain Madigas and even enlighten them over cultural past. They often narrate the exploits of the locally acclaimed proponents of the oppressed and their cultural significance. Thus, they try to recover the past glory of Madigas through narrative performances. One Dakkali Narsimulu lives on the fringes of Yalal village in Telangana. He narrates the stories by playing on kinnera. He claims: "I myself make the instrument for my use. I rear dogs for the purpose of hunting in the nearby forest. Occasionally I visit the neighbouring Madiga villages for food and money. I live with my family in a small hut."

In the outskirts of Shadnagar town, 8 Dakkali artistes from 14 families still play kinnera while narrating stories. This is the only town that comprises majority Dakkali population in the town. Besides their artistic narration, they also practise folk remedy for ailing persons in general and the Madigas in particular. They visit neighbouring villages and stay there for some days and collect *thyagam* or traditional honorarium from the Madiga families. They prepare makeshift arrangements in villages for their short stay. In Shadnagar, most of them have erected huts on a permanent basis. After visiting neighbouring villages, they come back to their huts in the town. Unlike in the past, they have got used to the urbanized milieu.

Sub-Caste Trinity: Comparative Perspective

The sub-caste trinity signifies three dependent castes of the Madiga community in Telangana state. This chapter aims at examining socio-cultural perspectives of the select dependent castes—Chindu, Baindla and Dakkali which still lie at the bottom of the caste-ridden society. The discussion is fused with the outcome of the research study that lasted more than two years.

Varna, caste and their fragmentations were evolved and emerged as sub-castes and dependent castes. They were further expanded into castes. They were institutionalized as a social system in India. The select dependent castes can be located in hierarchal order based on their sub-caste and socio-cultural status. Their artistic performances too signify the hierarchal considerations. In the social hierarchy of the select dependent castes, Dakkali occupies the third place given their social relations. In fact, Madigas are bound to patronize these sub-castes. In present time, the Madiga patronage is hardly extended to the dependent castes due to changing circumstances in social life. The relation between patron and client is such that patron caste should take care of the client castes/dependent castes while the dependent castes are bound to glorify the cultural history of the patron caste through their artistic performances. Now it is becoming a thing of rarity as the old generation is getting extinct.

Dakkalis are desirous of a change not only in their place in society but also in profession as well. Since most of them are still illiterate, they cannot go for better jobs. All that they find is labour work which fetches them a meagre income for living. Grim physical circumstances in villages have prompted them to migrate to cities where they are promised bread and butter through other means. Some aged Dakkalis who know only their hereditary occupation are unable to move to other places for new opportunities.

One person with commitment to his caste-based occupation is Mogulaiah who received the best Ugadi award from Chief Minister K. Chandrasekhar Rao. He also sang the title song for the Telugu film "Bhimla Nayak." This has drawn him into limelight. He plays the 12-fret instrument which is an elaborately painted and decorated one, affixed with a wooden turtle-puppet that bows, jumps and salutes the audience. A poor artiste with rural background, he kept representatives of 52 countries spell-bound with his music produced from his twelve-note kinnera. His twelve-hour concert played without respite was amazing. The life history of Mogulaiah, who hails from Gatturaipaakula village in Telakapally Mandal of Nagarkarnool district, is introduced in the academic syllabus for the 8th class students.

Though Mogulaiah has become popular, he is yet to overcome his economic misery. He lives in Hyderabad in a small rented tin-shed. He depends upon meager income of his son who is a rag-picker suffering from epilepsy. His daughter has lost her husband. He shared his agony with the *Andhrajothi*, the daily newspaper: "Members of my family often sleep without food. We live only on rice given on the ration card in my village. I have no money to pay rent and buy medicines for my ailing son. Sometimes members of my family are content with raw-chili paste in the meal as we cannot afford to buy vegetables. "My ailing wife died recently for want of better medical treatment. I had no money left in my hands to meet the expenses" (Vadlamudi n.p.). Other Dakkalis neither enjoy popularity from the public nor receive any financial support from any other source.

Dakkali Balamma, who recently passed away, was the only

woman performer among Dakkalis living in some districts of the Telangana State. "Even at 95, she played the instrument and sang the story of 'Panduga Sayanna' flawlessly." At most places, Dakkali performers are men while their women come along with bowls for begging food. Living on the outskirts of a remote village called Mumbapur in Vikarabad district, Balamma narrated the stories eulogizing the exploits of Panduga Sayanna, a social bandit who hailed from the Kapu caste (a dominant upper caste in Zadcherla district of Telangana). He was opposed to the hegemony of the opulent and the dominant. His belief was that the rich people had accumulated wealth which was ill-gotten. He stood by the poor and the oppressed. He looted the wealthy and distributed the riches to the poor.

Pandaga Sayanna was termed Telangana Robinhood. Even today, the history of Pandaga or Pandugolla Sayanna is intact, thanks to the nomadic tribes and dependent castes like Dakkalis who spread the exploits of the saviour of the downtrodden. The affluent sections of society branded Panduga Sayanna a bandit. Sayanna challenged the dominant and declared a war against them. He came to the rescue of those dying of hunger by attacking the wealthy people and distributing the booty among the poor. He made deadly weapons on his own and formed a militant troop for the cause. But the dominant forces connived with the government and got him assassinated.

Pandugolla Sayanna was born on the festive day of Dussehra and Muharram in a village called Merugoni of Navabpet Mandal in Mahabubnagar district in Telangana between 1840 and 1885. It is also said that Sayanna's mother did not have an issue for long, so she vowed during "Phir" (Phir is the Muslim fair) and Sayanna was born on Moharram day. So, the practice of preparing for "Kandura" on Muharram day began. He kept this 'Riwaj' for Kandura on Moharram day till he survived.

In order to prepare for "Kandura" that implies sacrificing of sheep and goats, he blocked the Tandur route and robbed twelve bastas (bags) of rice and six sheep flock from Golla Chennaiah. Golla fell at his feet and pleaded to return the same as he was a poor man and had a large family to feed. This sent a kind of hunger churning feel inside his stomach out of 'daya and jail or compassion and pity.' As Sayanna could feel the hunger cramps of the poor, so Golla was spared and his flocks returned" (Spoorthy).

"Common people opined that Pandugolla Sayanna was neither a thief nor a bandit. He was a 'Hero' of the poor people. He was a brave and heroic man who saved and reinstated poor people's health, wealth and lives. They considered him as their own blood relative" (Rao n.p.). It is said that Sayanna was active in rural sports and he would upturn the bullock cart easily. That time, the hegemony of the village chiefs was unleashed. Landlords seized the lands belonging to Pandugolla Sayanna. His family landed in trouble. An atrocity was carried against the aunt of Panduga Sayanna. The weaker sections were scared of the landlords. They never protested against the atrocities unleashed by the landlords.

Given the atrocious acts by the dominant sections in the village, Pandaga Sayanna raked up fire of his revolutionary battle. He was determined to challenge it. He became a militant and revolted against it. He forged a militant army against the Nizam. His sole aim was to wage war against the dominant forces. He had a clear idea as to why one should use weapons and why military struggle should take place. He wanted to create social awareness among the people on one hand and wage a war against the dominant forces on the other. He wielded weapon for the people's cause. He was a mature hero of the middle-class society. He was not an ordinary man in terms of his organic intellectuality. He was educated with a knowledge required for challenging the hegemonic forces. He was trained to dare the hegemonic classes. His message was that every person from the downtrodden section must be educated. He took up the scheme for supply of free food in order to alleviate the starvation of the poor which sowed the seed for emancipation of the poor through social revolution.

It was difficult for the dominant forces to digest the growing popularity of Sayanna among the downtrodden people. In the face of his popularity and his cause for the hapless, he was implicated in several false cases and was also imprisoned. Some people belonging to the Reddy community pressurized the Nizam and got Sayanna arrested. People resented the conspiracy to kill Sayanna with the help of Jangu Jalalkhan Mohiti Meensab, the Superintendent of Police. Some people pressurized Shankaramma, the queen of Wanaparthy, one of the districts in Telangana at present, to get Sayanna released from the jail.

The furious mob attacked the district jail but Sayanna was not lodged there. People revolted against the police. Wanaparthy Shankaramma stood by the people and met Meer Mahamud Ali, the Nizam king, and appealed to him to release Sayanna from the jail as per the wishes of the people. For Sayanna's release, a sum of Rs. 10,000 was to be deposited towards surety. Shankaramma agreed to pay. After bowing to the demand of the people, the Nizam government issued an order *'Maar Mat, Chodo.'* Shankaramma returned to Palamuru with supporters amidst fanfare. But landlords conspired again to do away with Sayanna at any cost. The stay order bearing *Maar Mat, Chodo* was modified to *Maar, Mat Chodo*, meaning that he should be killed and not spared. S.P. Mohithimeen Sab, Jangalal and a cunning patwari Venkat Rao were part of this conspiracy. They awarded death sentence to Sayanna. Finally, they beheaded Sayanna and threw his headless body elsewhere. The furious mob attacked the office of Superintendent of Police. The SP died of heart attack after seeing the irate mob around his office. The people set government hostel buildings on fire where the landlords Nagi Reddy, Venkat Rao, Peddi Reddy and Ram Reddy were celebrating. They were burnt to death.

Through the songs Balamma played the kinnera in tune with

the music, she narrated the story of Sayanna who was betrayed by a Madiga person called Tuppali. He sided with the landlords and was responsible for Sayanna's murder. This was a popular story which Dakkalis often narrated to the village people.

No historian recorded the history of Sayanna. It was simply dismissed as a folk story. Dalit artistes like Laxmaiah, Ramulu and nomadic Dakkalis could preserve it by singing songs. It is dalit dependent castes who shaped Sayanna's exploits into songs and continued to sing in his praise. Thus, Dakkali artistes have preserved the history of the saviours of the day.

Recently a novel was written in the local dialect of the people on the life of Panduga Sayanna based on the scantly available information. It is a notable legend among the folk. The novel is written by Bekkam Janardhan, an advocate by profession, hailing from Mahabubnagar district; he rewrote the history of the margins and deconstructed the dominant attitude through the Telugu literature by publishing a novel.

Chindus are basically performing artistes. But they strongly claim that they are the offspring of Madigas. They give performances in different veshams or roles on storylines. They narrate and perform stories like *Yekshaganam, Bhagavatham* and *Yellamma Katha*. They are matinee idols in their performances. Their make-up cost goes high because of the material they use. The Chindu population is highly concentrated in five districts of Telangana. They are found mostly in villages which are the source for their livelihood. Majority Chindu families depend upon non-traditional occupations and government pensions. Their complaint is that they don't have proper habitation and pensions are a mirage for them. Their performances have lost sheen because of the onslaught of the electronic media. The present generation is not much interested in legends and mythical stories.

Most of the Chindu artistes take to different professions to eke out their livelihood. Chindus of the first and the second generations hardly evince interest in their traditional performance.

It is because the profession demands dedication, discipline, adequate patience and love for art. The Chindu youth are deprived of all these essentials for lack of encouragement from public in general and from their patron community in particular. Chindu children are encouraged towards education. Some Chindu youth became government employees and built pukka houses. Some of them have built *pukka* houses while most of them live in the dilapidated mud shacks. Their women do agricultural labour. Dakkali women are trained to weave mats and baskets. They are not habituated to agricultural labour like Chindu women. Dakkali women were not allowed to work along with other castes. Of course, it is not a rigid practice now. However, they prefer to rear domestic animals which fetch them some lucrative money from the sale. Most of them are desirous for upward mobility.

Chindus do not treat Baindlas as untouchables. They are proud of their public performance. It is because several characters are involved in the performance which would draw large audience. Baindlas are endowed with artistic narrative techniques. Their narrative performance is related to ceremonies and rituals conducted on particular occasions. Their narrative performance involves mediation with the local deities. It reflects the local cultures of the margins. They come to the rescue of the Madigas with their priestly role when the Brahmins refuse to mediate with the Dalit gods during ceremonies.

On the other hand, the Chindus give a narrative performance only for Madigas and not for other castes. Of course, other castes can watch the Chindu performance in Madiga wadas. The performance is actually meant for their patron community. In some villages of Khammam district, Baindlas use musical instruments such as cymbals, a hand-harmonium and a percussion accompanied by Jamidika. The main narrator sings and dances while narrating the story of Yellamma, the folk goddess. Songs are shared by the chorus. In some villages of Mahabubnagar district, only two persons are involved with one Jamidika each.

The main narrator sings and the other narrator shares the song. The same Yellamma Katha can also be narrated through different methods. The mode of narration may be different but the essence of the myth is same. The dual narration of it is discernible across the district.

Yellamma Song

We pay obeisance to you, mother!
You are our Chindu Yellamma
We revere you a lot, always
Mother, you are synonymous with Chindu folk arts
Mother, you brought Chindu as your surname. (Mother)
We wish to behold your musical step in full view
We wish to hear when you sing in full throat
The devoted mass would delight when you play
All people would go in trance with your song. (Mother)
You dedicated your life to Chindu art
You played and sang abundantly Chindu art that was on extinction
You rejuvenated it to its peak. (Mother)
People grieve when your voice ceases
They wail when your voice goes mute
There are no people who do not remember you
We ever remember you. (Mother)
Mother, you have no death; you are immortal
You would ever live in Chindu folk arts. (Mother)

(Trans. from Telugu by the author)

The song is sung in praise of Yellamma goddess. The devoted masses offer their humble obeisance through prayers addressing the goddess as their mother. They venerate her with utmost respect as she is synonymous with Chindu folk arts. Chindu is the name that evolves from the vibrant dancing steps of the goddess. The people yearn to behold the musical steps in full view and hear her singing in full throat to their delight which would land them in trance. The goddess being dedicated to Chindu art plays and sings and enlivens Chindu art when it is on extinction. People are delighted and blessed with the songs of the goddess go disappointed and grieve when her voice becomes mute. The goddess is immortal and would continue to live in the Chindu folk arts forever.

Jamidika stands as a cultural representation of the Baindla community. It is due to the sub-caste disparity that there is no inter-dining between the Chindus and the Baindlas. Each of them has an independent culture for representation of their identity. The musical instruments of both the dependent castes stand as cultural metaphors. No marital relations exist between them. They strictly follow endogamy. In exceptional cases, inter-sub-caste marriages take place between the educated youth of these two communities.

Baindlas maintain priesthood for Madigas in their ceremonies and rituals while Chindus do not involve in any such ritualistic activities. Chindu elders perform priestly responsibilities during the Chindu marriage ceremonies. Chindus are hired by government departments to make use of their services to popularize the government schemes through their cultural performances among the general public in various villages of the state. Chindus have greater scope to pull the wider audience while Baindlas are limited to the temple precincts of Yellamma deity, where they keep singing and eulogizing the local goddesses. They get pittance for their narrative performance. Such celebrations are conducted on particular occasions in a year.

Baindlas do not spend much on their musical instruments or on the spaces of their performance. Temples of the local deities provide platforms for their performances. While playing music in tune with the narration, they pass instructions to the bridegroom and the bride in the wedding pandal. They play the Brahminical role in the ceremonies. This has nothing to do with Chindus who are only the performing artistes. The Baindla priests offer folk remedy to the people who are in possession of goddess. They prepare amulets for the ailing people to exonerate the bad spirits from their body. They are strong believers in the bad and good spirits.

Dakkalis take the third position in hierarchal order among the three dependent castes. They are treated as untouchables by the patron castes and other dependent castes as well. They do not mingle with other communities. Their habitations are located outside the village and they prefer to live in the vicinity of the Madiga ghettos. They too involve in hunting apart from narrating Veer Gathas or local legends including the story of Jambavamuni. They make their musical instruments themselves which do not cost much. The instruments produce multi-tunes. Unlike Baindlas and Chindus, Dakkalis tend to beg food from the Madiga community. Thyagam is a traditional payment made by the Madiga community for its dependent castes like Dakkalis based on performance. Some people make instant offers in appreciation of their narrative performances. It is because of the kind of relation they have with their audience. The fact is that Madigas and Dakkalis have patron-client relation from the ancestral period *per se*. It is Dakkalis who glorify the cultural history of Madigas. Dakkalis do not touch food from any other community while Baindlas and Chindus accept from other castes too. This could be a traditional norm of their caste. In the changing social scenario, the second and third generations of Baindla and Chindu communities do not follow their caste norms. Most of the young people are reluctant to beg food from their patron community.

In the same way, the patron community too does not encourage them to beg for food or money like their ancestors. They enlighten the dependent castes to involve in some work to earn their livelihood. The people of the older generation among Dakkalis would insist upon their 'Thyagam' or a traditional payment when their patrons were reluctant to pay it. But for the younger generation, expecting such traditional payment from their patrons is a matter of shame. Such payment was to be made in the name of tradition that continued through generations. This tradition is disappearing now. No Madiga villagers are prepared to follow the tradition which is scrapped with the old generations of the Dakkali communities in Telangana state.

This field-based research shed light on several facts. Major part of the research is attributed to intensive interactions with the select communities-Baindlas, Chindus and Dakkalis. All the three dependent castes of the Madiga community are not traced in all the districts of Telangana. Their habitations are located in the interior villages. The three sub-caste groups have not been found in the same village at a time. Like any other caste society, they too have the hierarchical order. Socio-cultural disparities are obvious even among the three dependent castes. Of the three, Dakkalis are the most oppressed untouchable group.

Given their socio-cultural relations with the Madiga patrons, Dakkalis too have a sense of superiority and inferiority. Dakkalis still remain inaccessible to the domestic holds of the Madiga community. No marital relations and collective dining with Madigas are acceptable even today. The new generation of the Dakkalis is reluctant to go by their ancestral occupation which hardly fetches expected livelihood through artistic narrative performances. Their narrative performances mainly focus on cultural glorification of the Madiga community.

In this changing social scenario, Dakkalis tend to become a part of the mainstream society. In other words, they dream for urbanization by changing their ancestral occupation. Aged Dakkalis still cling to their caste-based occupation with outmost reverence. Given their interest in the practice of story-telling for generations, they hardly fit into other modern professions. With the legacy of illiteracy and poverty, they cannot compete with the modern educated youth. The young Dakkali children are reluctant to follow their elder people. They prefer different professions and do not remain traditionally loyal to the Madiga community. They are keen to protect their self-respect. Thus, they look forward to pursuing upward mobility. Their population is dismal when compared to that of other two dependent castes.

Baindlas are also traced with no high population in the villages of Khammam and Nalgonda districts. Unlike Dakkalis, the Baindla community shares the Madiga ghetto. It is because Baindlas act as priests for Madigas on ceremonial occasions. There is no prohibition on inter-dining/collective dining but marital relations are not accepted. Madigas in villages still respect the Baindla-priesthood while the urban Madigas prefer Brahmin priests to perform worships and conduct rituals for them. The urban Madigas attempt to emulate the Hindu tradition. Baindlas have no place when Brahmin priests pitch into priestly performances. As a consequence, Baindlas are bound to lose their livelihood.

Thus, the Baindla tradition is on the verge of extinction. The village environment presents this situation today. It is because the elders of the first generation are dead and their children are not willing to promote it. Only a few of them are interested in story-telling pertaining to the goddess Yellamma even on occasional celebrations. In the absence of such celebrations, they tend to do labour work. Aged Baindlas in their love for story-telling cling to their tradition for the sake of the ancestral legacy. They have no other option but to cling to the tradition because they cannot do physical labour. Some Baindla youth have got government jobs. It is a rarest of the rare case that the Baindla person like Kadiam Srihari became a minister in the Kalvakuntla Chandrasekhar Rao cabinet in Telangana government. Young Baindlas prefer to pursue the lucrative modern profession in the mainstream social life. They are desirous of modern living. The wealthy educated Madigas are now engaging the local Brahmin priests to conduct ceremonies. In the act of upward mobility taken up by the educated rich Madigas, Baindlas along with other dependent castes are neglected. The young generation of the Madiga community is least bothered about their dependent community. Thus, the ancestral occupation does not promise livelihood for Baindlas.

The living standards of Chindus or the Chindu Madigas are little better than that of Baindlas and the Dakkalis. Though they are dependent on the Madiga community, their performances in different roles in *Yakshagana, Bhagavatha* and the *Ramayana*, bring acclaim to the cheering public. They spend a lot of money on costumes, colours and fake jewellery. They prefer to live in the vicinity of the Madiga ghettos. They feel that they are part and parcel of the Madiga community. They perform myths and legends in daytime with some audience around. The Chindu population is found more in Nalgonda district than in any other district of Telangana state. Some Chindu children, who are not interested in going to school, still carry forward this artistic occupation with their elders. The state government occasionally engages Chindu artistes in order to promote popular schemes among the public.

Very few of them are blessed with the *pukka* houses sponsored by the government. But some Chindu artistes have turned to shoe-making. This takes place for want of patronage and support either from Madigas or from the state government. Thus, they are confronted with occupational crisis. Most of the aged Chindu artistes depend upon the pensions distributed irregularly. There are some government employees too among Chindus. The Chindu women too involve in physical labour like any other woman from the lower caste. There are complaints that most of them have not been issued Aadhaar cards to be eligible for pensions. All three dependent artistes say in unison that electronic media is a curse for them as it dominates the traditional musical performances with its jarring music. It is depriving their artistic spirit and livelihood as well. Thanks to the surging effect of the modern electronic media, traditional occupations have almost disappeared and the livelihood of these artistes is precarious.

Annexure I

Project Field Survey District-Wise Data

1. Mahabubnagar

S. No.	Mandal and Village	Baindla families	Baindla artistes	Main occupation	Chindu families & artistes	Dakkali families	Dakkali artistes	Main occupation
1.	Bomma-rajupeta, Pollepally	4	2	Agri-Labour	—	1	1	Agri-Labour
2.	Bomma-rajupeta, Vadicherla	—	—	—	—	2	2	Agri-Labour
3.	Jargnagar, Shadnagar	—	—	—	—	14	5	Agri-Labour
4.	Yalal, Yalal	—	—	—	—	1	2	Agri-Labour

2. Nalgonda

S. No.	Mandal and village	Baindla families	Baindla artistes	Main occupation	Chindu families	Chindu artistes	Main occupation	Dakkali families or artistes
1.	Narketpally, Narketpally	—	—	—	15	08	Agri-labour	—
2.	Chundur, Nermet	—	—	—	16	06	Agri-labour	—
3.	Kalagallu, Darvespuram	—	—	—	07	05	Agri-labour	—
4.	Kalegallu, Pochampally	—	—	—	10	04	—	—
5.	Malley Pally, Chinnapake	04	02	Agri-labour	—	—	—	—
6.	Malley Pally, Angadipeta	05	03	Agri-labour	—	—	—	—
7.	Malley Pally, Gudipaka	03	01	Agri-labour	05	06	Agri-labour	—
8.	Nampally, Nampally	04	03	Agri-labour	06	06	Agri-labour	—
9.	Chintak Pally Venkatapeta	—	—	—	05	02	Agri-labour	—

3. Khammam

S. No.	Mandal and village	Baindla families	Baindla Artistes	Main occupation	Chindu families	Dakkali Families	Dakkali artistes	Main occupation
1.	Mudikonda, Pammi	1	06	Agri-Labour	—	—	—	—
2.	Mudigonda, Nela-Kondapally	04	02	Agri-Labour	—	—	—	—
3.	Konigarla, Pedagopathi	—	—	—	—	02	01	Agri-Labour
4.	Koda, Akupamula	—	—	—	—	02	01	Agri-Labour

4. Warangal

S. No.	Mandal and village	Baindla Families or artistes	Chindu families or artistes	Dakkali families	Dakkali artistes	Main Occupation
1.	Darmajagar Pekkapendayal	—	—	01	01	Agri-Labour
2.	Darmajagar Naskal	—	—	01	—	Agri-Labour

5. Medak

S. No.	Mandal and village	Baindla families or Artistes	Chindu families or artistes	Dakkali families	Dakkali artistes	Main occupation
1.	Siddipet, Siddipet	—	—	01	01	Agri-Labour
2.	Dekarakonnal Appireddy Pally	—	—	02	01	Agri-Labour

6. Adilabad

S. No	Mandal and Village	Baindla families or artistes	Chindu families or artistes	Dakkali families	Dakkali artistes	Main occupation
1.	Nirmal	—	—	02	01	Agri-Labour

7. Siricilla

S. No.	Mandal and village	Baindla families	Baindla artistes	Main occupation	Chindu families or artistes	Dakkali families or artistes
1.	Yellareddy Rajannapeta	03	02	Agri-Labour	—	—

8. Karimnagar

S. No	Mandal & village	Baindla families or artistes	Chindu families	Chindu artistes	Main occupation	Dakkali families	Dakkali artistes
1.	Siricilla Desaipally	—	04	03	Agri-labour	—	—

9. Siddipet

S. No.	Mandal and village	Baindla families or artistes	Chindu families	Chindu artistes	Main occupation	Dakkali families or artistes
1.	Thogutta Thukkapuram	—	02	02	Agri-labour	—

*Agri-labour = Agricultural Labour

A Map of the Districts Showing Concentration of the Dependent Castes

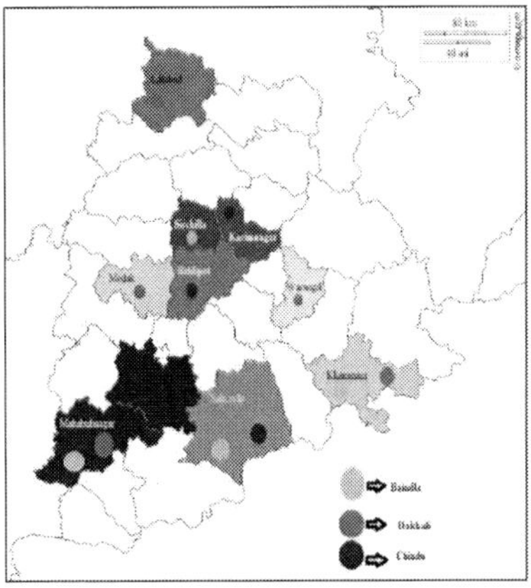

Annexure II
Empirical Data

A study was conducted in nine districts of Telangana state after identifying target groups through pilot survey. During the Telangana formation, some new districts have been created, which have also become part of the study. Accordingly, data was collected from various sources which include interviews with the elders of the communities. Close interactions with their families were conducted. The people of the dependent castes are spread all over the interior villages of various Mandals in the identified districts which prominently include Mahabubnagar, Nalgonda, Khammam, Warangal, Medak, Adilabad, Siricilla, Karimnagar and Siddipet.

Within Mahabubnagar district four mandals viz. Bomraspet, Polepally, Jahangir and Vadicherla have been identified with Baindlas and Dakkalis families. In this district, eighteen Dakkali families are traced. Of these families, 10 individuals are artistes who are still associated with their traditional occupation. Apart from this, they do agricultural labour as their main occupation during the season. But there are only four families of the Baindla community concentrated in Polepally village of Bomraspet Mandal. Only two individual artistes are active in their traditional occupation. On the whole, there are no Chindu families in the entire district of Mahabubnagar.

Four mandals viz. Narkatpally, Chundur, Kalagallu, Mallepally, Nampally and Chintapelly in Nalgonda district are concentrated with Baindla and Chindu families. 16 Baindla families are spread over Chinnapaka, Andadipet and Gudipeta villages in Mallepally Mandal. Of these sixteen families, only nine individuals are active artistes and the rest are associated with agricultural labour. In almost all Mandals in the district, 64

Chindu families are living. Of these, thirty-six people are artistes involving Chindu performance. They give performances as and when they are called by the neighbouring villages. There are no Dakkali families found in any village of the district.

Pammi and Nelakondapally of Mudigonda Mandal of Khammam district have fourteen Baindla families. Only eight individuals from these families are active in their artistic performances. Apart from their seasonal performances, they also do agricultural labour. In Pedagopati and Akupamula villages of Konagarala and Koda Mandals respectively, only four Dakkali families were residing and out of which only two individuals were active in their traditional occupation. However, agriculture is the main occupation of both Baindla and Dakkali families.

Pekkependyala and Naskal in Darmajagar Mandals of Warangal district have one Dakkali family in each village. There is only one artiste from two families. Agricultural labour is the main occupation of the Dakkali families. Baindlas and Chindus were not found in this Mandal and no information was available about them in any other place in the district. Siddipet and Dekarakonnal of Madak district have 3 Dakkali families with only two artistes from each family which is mostly associated with the agricultural labour. Thogutta, Thukkapuram of Siddipet Mandal have only two Chindu families with two artistes from each family. Nirmal Mandal in Adilabad district of the North Telangana has two Dakkali families having one artiste who still continues his traditional occupation while Yellareddy Rajannapeta in Siricilla District have 3 families that produced only two Baindla artistes. Agricultural labour is the main occupation of all the families. Four Chindu families have been located in Desaipally of Siricilla District. Of these four families, three were engaged in their ancestral occupation. No Dakkali families were traced in any part of the district.

The data collected across Telangana State clearly shows that all villages within the respective Mandals in each district have not been concentrated with all three dependent castes. Some villages do not have either of them. Though some of the individual artistes are found still clinging to their respective ancestral occupation, they engage in other means of livelihood and do agricultural labour during the harvesting season.

Research field work has been carried out on the three chosen categories of dependent castes in 8 districts of Telangana state. All the three dependent castes viz. Baindlas, Dakkalis and Chindus are not populated in all the districts equally. The data was collected after conducting survey in the districts. These dependent castes do not live right in the district headquarters but they live in interior places which are located far from the Mandal headquarters.

This project was intended to examine socio-cultural perspectives of dependent dalit communities associated with the Madiga community in some districts of Telangana State. All the three castes-Baildlas, Chindus and Dakkalis are dependent castes. However, there are obvious disparities in socio-cultural dimensions. The project also focused on aspects of social relations of the dependent castes with their patron community. The three castes are associated with the narrative and the performatory categories. Their artistic skill differs from one another. Their narrative performance is presented in a different way. The instruments and costumes used in their respective performances are unique to each other.

Society and Culture: The majority people of the state population speak Telugu. Urdu is also widely spoken in some parts of the state. The culture is a combination of Persian customs dating back to the period of the Mughals and the Nizams. Many Hindu festivals such as *Deepawali*, *Srirama Navami, Ganesh Chaturthi*, *Maha Shivaratri* and Muslim festivals such as *Bakra-Eid* and *Eid- ul-Fitr* are celebrated in this state. *Bataukamma* festival and *Lashkar Bonalu* are the state festivals of Telangana. The festival is celebrated every year to mark the Telangana culture and tradition. Language: Telugu is the official language of Telangana state. Some people claim that the Telangana Telugu is different from the Telugu language spoken in Andhra Pradesh. It is true that dialectically the language differs. The Telugu language includes words from Sanskrit, Urdu and English language. Urdu was the official language of Hyderabad before 1948, but after the Hyderabad state joined the Republic of India, Telugu became the official language of the state. Telugu is also the medium of instruction in schools and colleges. The present research was planned before the formation of Telangana. Before its formation, the state had only 10 districts. The government of Telangana reorganized the states keeping in view the political and administrative necessity of the people in the state. Thus, they are reorganized into thirty-three districts.

This research was taken up to explore socio-cultural perspectives of the dependent Dalit communities. In Telugu states, only two principal sub-castes which are immensely focused in literature have been explored. But no researcher has attempted to explore the socio-cultural predicament of the dependent castes which have been looked down upon by their patron castes in their social hierarchy. There are more than sixty sub-castes in the Dalit community in the Telugu states of Telangana and Andhra Pradesh. Of those recorded castes, three dependent castes viz. Baindlas, Chindus and Dakkalis have been selected for research study. In the beginning of the research, the select communities were surveyed and identified across the Telangana state. All three communities are not found same in many aspects of their life and performance across the state. These three sub-caste categories are sparsely seen across various Mandals in the districts.

Baindlas, Chindus and Dakkalis have been the most backward and neglected dependent castes of the Dalit community. No research was carried out from the comparative perspective of these social categories. Given the viability of the topic the ICSSR, New Delhi, sanctioned the project during 2015-2017. The Madiga community takes the patron role while dependent castes take client position in their socio-cultural and economic relations. Traditionally these highly marginalized castes depend upon the support of the patron community. They use their artistic performances in the glorification of Madiga culture and the narration of legendary stories relating to the local goddesses. Artistes of these dependent castes are not concentrated at one particular place but they are scattered in the remote villages of Telangana state. The research study has examined the socio-cultural disparities among the dependent castes and established comparative perspectives keeping in mind their artistic narrative performances and relational gradations.

Bibliography

Abedi, Zakir. "Dalit Autobiographical Narratives Figures of Subaltern Consciousness Assertion and Identity." *Contemporary Dalit Literature: Quest for Dalit Liberation.* New Delhi: Arise Publishers, 2010.

_. "Dalit Literature: The Voice of the Downtrodden." Web.

Ahuja, Ram. "Concept, Origin and Structure:" *Indian Social System.* Jaipur and New Delhi: Rawat, 1993.

Antonius, R. *Interpreting quantitative data with SPSS* London: Sage. Babu, Laban. Qtd. Darla Venkateswara Rao. "Locating Madigas in Jambapurana *Dalits and Social Marginalisation,*" ed. J. Bheemaiah. Aaviskar Publishers, 2012.

Bapuji. B.R. "Margins and Related Concepts." *Dalits and Social Marginalisation*, ed. J. Bheemaiah, Jaipur: Aavishkar Publishers, 2012.

Best, J.W. & Kahn, J. *Research in Education*, New Delhi: Prentice Hall of India, 2006

J. Bheemaiah, ed. "Introduction." *Dalits and Social Marginalization.* Jaipur: Aavishkar Publishers, 2012.

_____. *Asamanatalu Adhikaralu:* Dalita Samika Vyasalu. Hyderabad: Prajasakti Daily Printing Press, 2006, Bridget Somekh & Cathy Lewin.

_____. *Research Methods in the Social Sciences*, London: Sage, 2005. Dangle, Arjun. ed. "Introduction." *Poisoned Bread.* Hyderabad: Orient Longman, 1992.

Das, Sisir Kumar. "Introduction." *Translating Caste: Stories, Essays, Criticism*, ed. Tapan Basu. New Delhi: A Katha Class Room Text, 2002.

Deo, Veena. "Dalit Literature in Marathi." Handbook of Twentieth Century Literature of India, ed. Nalini Natarajan. Greenwood Press, USA, 1996.

_. "Dalit Literature in Marathi." *Hand Book of Twentieth Century Literature of India*, ed. Nalini Natarajan.

Ghurye, G.S. *Caste and Race in India*. Bombay: Popular Prakashan, 1999.

Kannabiran, Kalpana. "Sociology of Caste and the Crooked Mirror: Recovering B.R. Ambedkar's Legacy." *Economic and Political Weekly*. 44: 4. Jan. 24-30, 2009.

Kistaiah, Gaddam, qtd. Chindula Yellamma: *Chindu Yakshagana Prasthanam* by Gaddam Mohan Rao. Hajipur: Chindu Pub., 2013.

Kota Shyamala Kama Sastry, Sri Andhra Vachaspathyamu (Tel), Vol. IV, K.S.K Sastri and Sons, 1940.

Ilaiah, Kancha. *Buffalo Nationalism: A Critique of Spiritual Fascism*. Kolkata: Samya, 2004.

Leedy, Paul D. *Practical Research: Planning and Design*, New York: Macmillan; London: Collie Macmillan, 1989.

Limbale, Sharankumar. *Towards Aesthetics of Dalits Literature: History, Controversies and Considerations*. Hyderabad: Longman, 2004.

Nicholas, William. *Research Methods: The Basics*. London: Routledge, 2011.

Punekar, Rohini Mokashi. ed. "On the Threshold: The Songs of Chokhamela." *Untouchable Saints: An Indian Phenomenon.* Manohar, New Delhi, 2005.

Malinowski, B. *Argonauts of the Western Pacific*. London: Routledge and Kegan Paul,1922.

Marshall, Catherine and Gretchen B. Rossman. *Designing Qualitative Research*, London: Sage, 1999.

Mimroth, P.L. "Use of word 'Harijan' objected." *The Hindu.* Sunday, September 28, 2003.

Mohan Rao, Gaddam. *The Hindu*, Friday Review published in Chindula Hamsa. Hajipur: Chindu Publications, 2013.

Prakash, *Bonala. Baindla Katha-Gaanam.* Hyderabad: Rahul Publications, 2012.

Schwandt, T. A. *The Sage Dictionary of Qualitative Inquiry*, Thousand Oaks, California: Sage, 2007.

Singh, Ekta. "Caste System in India: A Historical Perspective." Delhi: Kalpaz Publications.

Sonnad, Subhash R. "Caste." *Encyclopedia of Community: From the Village to the Virtual World*, ed. Karen Christensen & David Levinson. Vol. 1. Sage, 2003.

Shyamala, Gogu, ed. 'Thaataki' *Nallaregadi Sallu: Madiga Upakulala Adolla Kathalu*. Hyderabad: Mysamma Sabbanda, 2006.

Sridhar V. Ketkar. *History of Caste in India*. New Delhi: Cosmo, 1979.

Seetaramulu, Gurram. "Translating Jambapurana: The Cultural Genealogies of Madiga, Memory, History and Identity," unpublished Ph.D. thesis, English and Foreign Languages University, Hyderabad, August 2015.

Subhadra, Jupaka, ed. 'Maanyam,' *Nallaregadi Sallu: Madiga Upakulala Adolla Kathalu*. Hyderabad: Mysamma Sabbanda, 2006.

Swathi, Vadlamudi. "Kinnera's Last Strum," *The Hindu*, 27-08-2017.

Thirumala Rao, Jayadheer (ed). *Dakkali Jambapuranam*. Hyderabad: Janapada Prachurana, 2011.

_____. "Samaantara Samskritika Darpanam." *Dakkali Jambapuranam*. Hyderabad: Janapada Prachurana, 2011.

_____. "Vanishing Folk Art of Andhra Pradesh-Baindla." *Baindla Katha Gaanam*" by Bonala Prakash. Katha-Jamukula Katha, organised by STEPARC: Sphoorthi Theatre for Educational Puppetry, Art & Craft, Hyderabad. STEPARC is a voluntary organisation using puppetry and puppets as medium of Educative tools on April 21, 2012. www,pshoorthithearte.com.

_____. "Telangana Robin Hood-Panduga Sayanna." Organised by STEPARC. September 21, 2012. www, pshoorthitheatre.com.

Thurston, Edgar. *Castes and Tribes of Southern India*. Vol. II (C to J). Madras: Government Press, 1909.

Venkateswara Rao, Darla. 'Locating Madigas in Jambapurana.' *Dalits and Social Marginalisation*, ed. J. Bheemaiah. Jaipur: Aavishkar Publishers, 2011.

Zelliot, Eleanor and Rohini Mokashi Punekar, ed. 'Introduction.' *Untouchable Saints: An Indian Phenomenon*. New Delhi: Manohar, 2005.